YOU CAN HANDLE IT

10 Steps to Shift

STRESS

From Problem to
Possibility

Margaret Wehrenberg, PsyD
bestselling author of *The 10 Best-Ever Anxiety Management Techniques*

Copyright© 2017 Margaret Wehrenberg, PsyD

Published by:
PESI Publishing & Media
PESI, Inc.
3839 White Ave.
Eau Claire, WI 54703

Cover Design: Amy Rubenzer
Editing: Marietta Whittlesey
Layout: Jennifer Wilson-Gaetz & Amy Rubenzer

Proudly printed in the United States of America
ISBN: 9781683730651

PESI Publishing & Media
www.pesipublishing.com

About the Author

Margaret Wehrenberg, PsyD, is an international trainer and speaker on topics related to psychotherapy for anxiety and depression, stress management and on optimizing anxiety for achievement. She is a practicing psychologist, coaching for anxiety management and providing psychotherapy for anxiety and depression disorders. She has been training therapists for 25 years, and is a sought-after speaker for continuing education seminars, consistently getting the highest ratings from participants for her dynamic style and high quality content.

In addition to *You Can Handle It: 10 Steps to Shift Stress From Problem to Possibility*, she is a frequent contributor to the award-winning *Psychotherapy Networker* magazine and has produced *Relaxation for Tension and Worry*, an audio file for breathing, muscle relaxation and imagery to relax. Audio and DVD versions of her trainings are available from PESI. She has written several books on topics of anxiety and depression, including bestselling *The 10 Best-Ever Anxiety Management Techniques* and *The 10 Best Anxiety Busters*.

Table of Contents

What Is Stress, When Is It a Problem, and What Can You Do About It?

Stress is a Condition of Living

It's a fact: Life is stressful. Work life, home life, school life—no one is immune. Good news, bad news, even no news can trigger stress. Think about it. Good news makes us feel excited and the excitement shows in physical signs: our heart rate picks up and our breathing intensifies. Alternately, when someone is upset with us, the same physical response occurs: our heart rate speeds up and our breathing changes. Yet one stressful event is perceived as pleasant, the other unpleasant. Therefore, physical reaction alone does not determine whether the stress is damaging. Any force exerted on our minds or bodies that causes a reaction could be considered a stress, whether it is a physical force, such as a weight we are lifting, or an emotional force, such as breaking up an important relationship.

Stress is Useful

- When we stress muscles they get stronger, more flexible, and more resilient.

- When we stress our wit or intellect, we learn and acquire knowledge.

- When we stress the limits of our abilities, whether mental, artistic or physical, we often break through to higher levels of knowledge, creativity or strength. Plus, we get *better* at living our lives to the fullest.

Stress is Positive

In short, stress becomes positive when it challenges us to raise our current level of abilities and to grow. In order for stress to be positive, the challenge becomes threefold for us. We must:

- Resolve any problems.

- Respond to the demand.

- Control the situation and its effects on our lives

When we respond to positive stress, we grow from the experience and believe more in ourselves and our abilities.

Stress is Destructive

When people say they are experiencing stress, they typically mean the disruptive, destructive kind of stress. A stressor is an alarm, a signal for change in the body to cope with the stressor. When the body receives the alarm signal, there is an immediate physical response. A part of the brain, called the hypothalamus initiates the increases in heart rate and respiration that we call "fight or flight" if the stressor is a strong one. It also initiates a flow of adrenalin and cortisol to fuel that running or fighting.

Brief, even intense, alarm is not destructive to your health. But chronic stress will damage your health in many ways. When people say they are "stressed out" they mean this kind of chronic, damaging stress. We feel this way when there is too much pressure to push ourselves beyond reasonable goals. We feel overburdened, less able to respond. This kind of damaging stress occurs when you feel little or no control in situations you face. The degree of "stressed out" feeling is directly proportional to feeling you can influence the outcome of your situation. You might have the kind of inner peace that says, "If I have no control, then I can relax because there is nothing I can do," but most people find that hard to achieve.

Do You Have Any of These Physical or Emotional Symptoms?

Circle the typical severity of the symptom on a scale of 1–10
1 = mild/infrequent and 10 = severe/frequent

Headache	1	2	3	4	5	6	7	8	9	10
Muscle tension	1	2	3	4	5	6	7	8	9	10
Back pain	1	2	3	4	5	6	7	8	9	10
Indigestion	1	2	3	4	5	6	7	8	9	10
Diarrhea	1	2	3	4	5	6	7	8	9	10
IBS (Irritable Bowel Syndrome):	1	2	3	4	5	6	7	8	9	10
Appetite change	1	2	3	4	5	6	7	8	9	10
Jaw tightening, tooth clenching or grinding (TMJ):	1	2	3	4	5	6	7	8	9	10
Muscle weakness	1	2	3	4	5	6	7	8	9	10
Fatigue	1	2	3	4	5	6	7	8	9	10
Insomnia	1	2	3	4	5	6	7	8	9	10
Irritability	1	2	3	4	5	6	7	8	9	10
Easily angered	1	2	3	4	5	6	7	8	9	10
Anxious/depressed	1	2	3	4	5	6	7	8	9	10
Poor concentration	1	2	3	4	5	6	7	8	9	10
Make more mistakes	1	2	3	4	5	6	7	8	9	10
Accident prone	1	2	3	4	5	6	7	8	9	10

The higher your rankings and the more symptoms you endorse, the greater the likelihood that stress is negatively affecting your life.

Stress Affects You in Many Ways

Sadly, when you are negatively stressed, self-care diminishes. People often stop exercise regimens, their eating patterns change, and they drink more alcohol or caffeine. And worse, over time, poor self-care affects the *quality* of life. You may become less energetic, gain or lose weight, and lose the general feeling of good health. For some, self-worth plummets. And when you stop feeling good physically and emotionally, damaging stress has taken over your life and put you on a destructive path.

If negative stress levels continue for very long, tension builds and physical symptoms of stress occur. Such physical symptoms vary and range from mild to severe. An important 2016 study, jointly done with Purdue University and the University of Copenhagen, investigating the outcome of overwork on thousands of Danes, clearly demonstrated that when people started to work longer hours, and feel stress from the work, their risks for cardio-vascular disease, strokes, injuries and many other kinds of illnesses soared.

What Kinds of Stress Are You Experiencing?

When people feel as if life is too much, they may be experiencing what I call "Quantity Stress" or "Quality Stress." These situations occur when:

- ***When the numbers of expectations are too many you may feel quantity stress.*** When too many tasks, too many projects or too many chores pile up you may feel stress from the sheer volume of things to be done. You may not feel there are enough hours in the day to get everything done. You may have agreed to be two places at once and both obligations seem important. Then damaging stress hits.

- ***When the type of expectations is beyond your abilities you may feel quality stress.*** When you are assigned a project that you do not have the skills to complete, you do not feel capable and that is stressful. You could be asked to take care of a problem that you do not know how to solve. You could be faced with a physical burden that is beyond your strength. You may have to take a test on material you do not understand or cannot learn quickly enough. Then damaging stress hits.

Quantity Stress: When Life Is Too Much

- Have you ever felt you were expected to do too much?

- Did all your teachers assign tests or papers in the same week?

- Did you ever look at your desk and see more projects than you could clear off?

How did that make you feel about doing the work? How did it make you feel about your life? How did it make you feel about your abilities? The stress that results from this work *beyond your capability to produce* is *quantity stress*. You are able to do the work, but cannot complete it in the allotted time. If you are running a household, your stress probably falls into this category, especially if you are a parent who works at an income-producing job in addition to your work to keep the home and household running. Not only is childcare on the list, but there are endless details such as yard work, shopping, cooking, cleaning, chauffeuring children, repairing what is broken, etc. There is just too much to do in the allotted time! Your daily income work falls into this category, too. With downsizing and 'right-sizing,' employees at all levels of responsibility have had to take on the work another employee previously did without being given more time to do it (and typically not receiving more money for the extra work either).

Why is this so stressful? You *know* you can do each separate task! All together there are just *too many responsibilities for the time you have.*

- If you are an hourly wage earner, you are pressured to get the work done without overtime. You get even higher stress from your resentment over lost income.

- If you are salaried, how do you distinguish the reasonable number of hours to be on the job? You and your family both end up resenting your time at work. If you opt to maintain family time, you also get tense over fear your boss will decide you are not putting in enough time or that you are not getting enough done.

- If you are a student, you pull all-nighters, procrastinate over the work that feels overwhelming, and get too tired to do well on any of it.

- If you are a homemaker and stay-at-home parent, you may feel incompetent or inadequate because your goals for parenting, house-keeping and community involvement may exceed your time. You may be angry at the tasks you face without enough help from other family members.

- Social media strain: Have you ever wondered why everyone showing you glimpses of their lives on social media look so very happy, so successful compared to you and your family? Do you ever feel anger, guilt or fear that you are missing out on the happy life you see shining over these pictures of vacations, completed projects, celebrations and everyday super-happy lives? You may not believe you will ever achieve the glowing life so obviously led by everyone else who is posting photos and messages. When would you have time for it all?

Quality Stress: When Life Is Too Hard

- You are expected to work beyond your ability or experience.

- You are studying a subject that is beyond your preparation for the course or beyond your ability to learn it.

- You are faced with a family need, such as nursing someone or handling a budget crisis that is beyond your knowledge about what to do.

If this is happening to you, you face another type of unwelcome stress: *Quality Stress.* Most people have faced at least one knowledge crisis in student life, and most adults have faced a home maintenance or repair situation, such as a burst pipe that brought them face to face with a problem they could not solve alone. Perhaps preparing taxes required more than your knowledge of tax codes and options. Those situations are stressful, but will not usually cause you to question your worth. You will not expect yourself to know every fact or to be a plumber or an accountant. But when facing demands in your job beyond your ability that you think you *should be able to handle*, you may question your worth and value and feel in jeopardy of losing your job. This can happen if:

- You are frequently given tasks without sufficient training to perform them.

- You are given a project that requires you to learn too many new skills at once. Then you have to delay the project completion or revise deadlines while you learn these skills.

- Your job evaluation is subjective and you cannot determine if the supervisor views you as competent.

Worries about what will happen to your evaluation or even about whether you will be fired can cause tremendous stress. In work settings you often cannot change the stressor, nor diminish the impact, so damage occurs.

Quality Stress Solutions Depend on How You Cope

Faced with inability to change the circumstance, do you:

- ❑ Freeze and do nothing
- ❑ Procrastinate
- ❑ Overeat
- ❑ Use more alcohol or do drugs to relax after work
- ❑ Sleep too much or stop sleeping
- ❑ Get distracted, inefficient, confused and indecisive on the job

If you recognize these as coping skills, you are making your quality stress MORE damaging.

What Can You Do About Quantity or Quality Stress?

Learn the **10 Steps** that will immediately reduce your stress. These methods will help you eliminate stress and decrease the damage of stress by learning to:

- Manage the physical and emotional sensations of stress.

- Reduce the stress of unexpected or difficult situations.

- Eliminate the cause of your stress by:
    a. assessing what got you into the problem situation and
    b. creating a plan to avoid the circumstances.

It is rare that a situation causing negative stress cannot be improved. You get stress relief just knowing that you can prevent the situation in the future.

Stress management is not as complicated as you might think. Small changes will make a big difference. So, don't let the idea of learning stress management stress you out. It is easy to learn and easy to apply.

In *You Can Handle It* you will:

- Find methods and techniques you can easily learn.
- Lighten your stress immediately, even when the circumstances in your life cannot change immediately.
- Find stress reduction tools you can use at work and at home.
- Get help to evaluate the sources of your stress.
- Discover options for improving stress management.
- Get clear instructions about implementing the ideas.
- Practice and improve your stress management ability.

Remember, stress is a condition of living.

- Don't expect to eliminate stress forever.
- Do expect to handle whatever unwelcome stress comes your way.
- And … You can handle it!

Breathe

Breathe

Breathing is the Key

You can control your reaction to stress and deliberately induce relaxation, and all you have to do is breathe. You may say to yourself, "I already know how to breathe, I'm alive." Well, of course, you do. And many athletes or fitness buffs believe they already know about breathing because of their workout regimen, but when you are under stress one of the first things affected is breathing.

You may hold your breath, breathe in gulps or gasps, hyperventilate, breathe shallowly, or do some combination of these. And, chances are your stressed-out breathing is making it more difficult to respond to a stressor rather than improving your stress response.

Most people have not paid careful attention to how breathing changes when they are under pressure for a long time, such as when working on a project that is taking months to complete, caring for a sick family member, or living with someone who has an addiction. Under such conditions you may have changed your general way of breathing.

The first part of this method is to carefully observe how you breathe. Take a moment to write down what you observe about your breathing right now. The worksheet will give you some ideas of how to pay attention. Is your breathing regular in its pace on inhaling and exhaling? Do you pause in your breathing? When? Do you feel short of breath or rushed? Can you tell if you are filling your lungs or breathing into your chest only? What can you notice?

Then, the next time you are under pressure, set aside a part of your attention to observe how your breathing changes when you are tense:

- If you have to speak at a meeting and that makes you nervous, notice your breathing.

- If you are having a disagreement, note how you breathe.

- If you are feeling pressured from lack of time, take a moment to feel your breathing.

It may surprise you to find that you have not been filling your lungs or that you have been holding your breath when you inhale. The worksheet is to help you notice changes in your breathing.

Why Does Breathing Work So Well?

It may help to know that when stress is strong enough to trigger worried or anxious and panicky feelings, your body reacts without conscious intention. Your heart rate picks up, your breathing automatically increases, and changes in your adrenalin levels can make you feel shaky or jittery. You can control your breathing deliberately, and by doing so you can change all the negative physical aspects of stress.

Breathing Will Help If You Are Stressed Out by Fear

If you are panicky, whether you are in a situation that is objectively frightening or whether you are experiencing a panic attack with no objective cause, the stress response is intense, matching the degree of fear you feel. Your body is instantaneously ready to run from or fight off the cause of the fear. Fear triggers a rapid spike in sympathetic nervous system activity, increasing heart rate, respiration, and blood pressure, and decreasing blood flow to the gut. It triggers a burst of adrenalin to magnify energy.

Breathing will ward off that physical response to fear by reducing heart rate, slowing adrenalin output, lowering blood pressure, restoring blood flow to the digestive system and thereby reduce the likelihood of a headache, dizziness or stomach upset. The most important outcome of breathing the relaxed way is that it sends your body a physical message to settle down. Taking deep, slow inhalations with even slower exhalations through the mouth is a breathing mechanism to stimulate the vagus nerve, which initiates the calming action of the parasympathetic nervous system.

My Breathing

Take a moment to write down what you observe about your breathing right now. Put a check mark next to all of these that apply:

- ❑ Short
- ❑ Even, but Fast
- ❑ Shallow
- ❑ Panting
- ❑ Gulping
- ❑ Hyperventilating

- ❑ Gasping
- ❑ Relaxed
- ❑ Long in, Short out
- ❑ Impeded
- ❑ Short in, Long out
- ❑ Holding

What I noticed about my breathing: _____

_____

_____

_____

_____

_____

How my breathing changed when I became tense:

- ❑ Short
- ❑ Even, but Fast
- ❑ Shallow
- ❑ Panting
- ❑ Gulping
- ❑ Hyperventilating

- ❑ Gasping
- ❑ Relaxed
- ❑ Long in, Short out
- ❑ Impeded
- ❑ Short in, Long out
- ❑ Holding

Breathing Is Also Important to the Non-Panicky Kind of Stress

Chronic stress causes you to tense up, giving a message to the muscles to "move!" Taking physical action to handle the problem is a natural response to an incoming stress signal. (It is not called the 'fight or flight' response for nothing.) However, chronic stress situations may not allow for physical responses. You might be tethered to a desk for weeks on end, kept close to the bedside of someone who is ill, or you might yourself have an injury that sidelines you. When your muscles are preparing to move, they contract, but if you then do not move them, that contraction results in tight muscles throughout your body. You will learn about muscle relaxation in the next chapter, but it starts with the breath, and, once breathing gets associated with relaxation, you can initiate immediate relaxation of muscle tension by breathing diaphragmatically.

Also, any kind of stress can make you distracted, increasing tendencies to worry over things that you cannot control. Focus on your breath centers you, redirecting your attention to the breathing rather than the situation you are stressing out over. Your mind will start to calm down. You may also associate breath with imagery of peace. Once breathing is associated in your mind with peace, you can trigger a peaceful state just by starting the breathing pattern.

Simple to Do, Hard to Remember

Practice to Master Breathing. You'll notice more about your breathing as you practice the following breathing technique. This technique is simple to do, but not easy to master. For breathing to effectively reduce tension, you first have to remember to use it! Until it becomes a habit, most people forget to breathe under anxiety or tension. It takes some time for this process to become smooth and easy. Breathing effectively requires practice and attention until it comes naturally. But once you have it down, this technique can be done anywhere, any time. Whether you are tense at work or home, in public or in private, you can breathe!

Diaphragmatic Breathing Technique:

1. To learn how it feels to breathe correctly for tension reduction, it is best to lie down flat on your back or stand in a relaxed manner, feet slightly apart, knees loose. You must have a straight passage for air to flow.

   Once you have mastered the feel of such breathing in a lying down or standing position, try it sitting upright to see if you need to make any adjustments. When you try this sitting down, make sure you are sitting straight, and that your head is upright, not dropping forward or tilted back against a couch cushion.

2. Notice how it feels to fill the lungs deeply. You may rest your hand on your abdomen. This will help you to notice if you are breathing deeply enough and whether your chest is tight. One way to get a sense of filling your lungs deeply is to think about how a balloon fills with water when you attach it to a faucet. The bottom fills and widens first, the balloon becomes heavy with it, and then the water fills the upper portion.

   This image of heaviness suggests how to imagine your breath. Form an image of your breath filling your abdomen, feeling heavy and warm. This will help your body to relax and fill your lungs completely. If you cannot get a sense of this, raise your arms over your head, lace your fingers together, and then take a slow deep breath. You will immediately feel the breath fill your lungs.

3. Next, blow out all the air in your lungs until you feel empty. Imagine or *actually do* this: buy a bottle of bubbles with a wand, and blow the bubbles. That gentle slow exhale that gives you lots of bubbles is just right for diaphragmatic breathing.

4. Then, begin to breathe in. Inhaling must be done evenly, as if you can fill your lungs from bottom to top in equal, even amounts. It will help you to breathe evenly if you find a pace that works to measure your breathing in and out. Count the time for breathing until you feel exactly full (but not over-full), measuring seconds without a stopwatch, by saying "1 - 1000, 2 - 1000, 3 - 1000, etc.," to get a measured, even breath.

   Chances are, you will take between 3-6 counts to fill your lungs with smooth inhalations. Those who have asthma or COPD of any type, do not add the stress of counting. Instead, use two sentences such as, "Now I breathe in all that is peace. Now I breathe out all that is not of peace." Or, "Smell the roses. Blow out the candles." Thinking those words, let your breath follow along.

5. Regardless, of your capacity to breathe, you may prefer to just think a word and breathe with it. On the in-breath, think "Here" and on the out-breath think the word "Now" or use the words "Calm - Strong" on the in-breath and out-breath.

6. Fill up evenly, no gulps or gasps, until you feel full but not tense and then release the breath at an even, measured pace, taking a bit longer to exhale than it took to inhale. Your body needs time to release carbon dioxide, and inhaling without enough time to exhale can make you dizzy.

   You may release your breath for two counts longer than it took you to inhale. The only change you make to the even pacing of inhalation and exhalation is that you may pause for two counts at the end of your breath. Do not pause between inhaling and exhaling and do not exhale faster than you inhaled. Either of those habits defeats the purpose of breathing to slow the stress response.

7. Using this breathing is a way to practice and increase mindfulness (being in the moment) and it becomes an overall stress reliever. Try this: Take note of your tension level and rate its severity on a scale of 0-10, with 10 being the most tense. Practice breathing for a few minutes. (If you can manage 5 minutes that would be an excellent amount of time to see the results.)

You will find that you repeatedly have other thoughts enter in, so when you notice your mind wandering, just say to the thought that came in, "Thanks," and immediately return your attention to the breathing. Knowing your mind will again remind you of what you need, and that you can safely focus on the breath for a few minutes, you can let go of any thought that takes your attention from your breathing. Then rate your tension level again. What do you notice?

It is essential to breathe the moment stress begins to build, so you must practice this relaxation breathing frequently, whether or not you are stressed at the moment. While you build your repertoire of stress-relief techniques, you will practice much more often than you will need to later.

How Will You Develop Your Breathing Technique?

Nowadays, we have fantastic aids to focus and guide breathing practice. At this time, there are many apps that can be downloaded to your hand-held or tablet devices. These vary in the image they provide or the tones or music that go with them, but you can easily find one you like. While new apps are always being developed, currently, a few popular apps that you might check out include:

- Breathe2relax
- Relaxlite
- Mycalmbeat
- Calm
- Paced Breathing

The goal is not to breathe like this all day, but to become able to remember and choose to breathe in this calming way. So, for a week, practice this breathing every day for 1-2 minutes at a time, up to 10 times a day.

You can set a reminder on any device to take a break every 90 minutes or just decide to practice whenever:

- You are stopped at a stop light.

- On hold on the phone.

- You finish brushing your teeth.

- You watch a program: Pick 1 show a day and practice before and after it.

- You are waiting in line at a store.

- You are waiting for a class or meeting to start at work or school.

- You are waiting in the car to pick up someone.

- You are washing your hands.

Next, it is helpful to start increasing the length of time that you practice breathing. There are two reasons for this. If you tend toward panic, breathing will interrupt and slow panicky feelings, but you need to sustain diaphragmatic breathing for a few minutes to do that. And if you want to begin a mindfulness meditation, this kind of breathing can help you get started with mindfulness. So, after about a week of regular practice for breathing, pick one time of day when you can predict that you will be uninterrupted for a few minutes. For most people it works best to pick early morning, late evening or your lunch break.

If you cannot predict such a time, take a look at your expectations of yourself. Do you really have a schedule that does not allow 5-10 of predictable quiet time? Is this because you do not plan or take the time or is it because you allow many interruptions? If so, the next stress-relieving step is to insist to those around you, whether family or colleagues, that they *must* leave you alone for 10 minutes with no exceptions. If you cannot imagine doing that, go on to Method 3 on Assertiveness!

During this uninterrupted period each day you are going to add one minute of breathing per day. For the second week, you will continue the 1-2 minute practices 7-9 times a day, but you will add one minute each day to the time you picked when you can be uninterrupted. By the end of the week, you may be breathing for 5-7 minutes. You would benefit if you could breathe for

10 minutes in this way. The goal is to achieve the physical calm that comes with brief, sustained breathing. During this time, you may have music on of a type that would enhance your relaxation. This period of time is the foundation for profound relaxation, meditation, and ultimately enabling you to cue with one breath the relaxation that you will practice in Method 2. Breathing will become your entry to instant stress reduction.

Learning to Breathe

No doubt about it: you will encounter obstacles before you make breathing work for you. Some of the common obstacles include:

1. **Forgetting to practice.** This is why it is suggested you begin to link breathing to MANY times and places and activities throughout the day. When you make a plan to practice breathing, actually visualize yourself practicing in your mind. Imagine yourself breathing at the sink, in the car, in front of the computer, on the phone or in front of the TV. This will help remind you to practice in those places. Then keep a note card handy and make a tally mark whenever your practice. The reinforcement of noticing when you practice will also set it more clearly in your mind and help you remember the next practice more readily.

2. **You get anxious when you breathe deeply.** This is not uncommon and, if it continues for long, indicates that you need a professional psychotherapist who may help you with the sources of your stress. Deep breathing tends to open up the very emotions that the tension has been holding down. In part, that is the purpose of breathing. Letting go of stress means releasing emotional as well as physical tension. You cannot let go of emotions that you do not recognize, *but if you did not want to feel them*, your anxiety and tension may increase rather than decrease as those unwanted emotions come too close to the surface. If this happens to you, find someone with whom you can talk out the anxiety caused by breathing.

3. **The breathing does not seem to help.** It is very rare for deep breathing to have no positive impact on stress reduction, but if you have this reaction ask someone to watch you breathe. The chances are good that you are

either filling your chest while keeping your abdomen tight or holding your breath during part of the breath. I once encountered two graduate students who insisted they must hold in their stomachs while breathing in. It did not fit their image of how to be pretty and feminine to let their abdomen move out when anyone was looking. When they took intentional breaths, they were doing the exact opposite of what their bodies would have done naturally. They were amazed to see how different it felt when they learned to let their abdomen expand while inhaling. An observer may notice this kind of a problem that you would miss on your own.

4. **You cannot concentrate when practicing your breathing.** Thoughts flit through your mind, distracting you, making you forget what you were doing. When you are adding a minute a day, this is especially likely. The best way to handle this is as follows:

- Notice that you have been distracted.

- Mentally say to yourself, "Oh. A distraction." Just notice, with no judgment against yourself for becoming distracted. Do not feel upset with yourself or impatient with the breathing. Imagine thoughts as clouds in the sky, just drifting by and you have no need to stop them.

- Redirect your attention to your breath.

- Focus on the physical sensation of breathing, notice the feeling of your lungs expanding, the sensation of feeling your waistband or of noting how your back shifts against a chair, etc. Feel the breath move through your nostrils or out of your mouth.

- Count to measure the pace to help keep your focus on the breath.

5. **You feel as if you cannot fill your lungs completely.** See the page about managing obstacles to breathing. If you have a respiratory problem requiring medical attention, you will, of course, need to take care of it medically. But if, in the absence of physical limitations, you feel restrictions such as feeling tight, or sense an obstruction as if there is a block in the airflow complete the following worksheet.

Helpful Breathing Tips

If you feel restrictions such as feeling physically tight, or sense an obstruction as if there is a block in the airflow be sure that:

  a. You are seated or standing upright with your neck straight aligned with your spine
  b. If you are lying down, do not have a pillow under your head. You may have one under your knees without restricting airflow.
  c. You loosen any restrictive clothing, such as tight jeans or neckties.

If those obvious solutions do not solve the problem, the source of the problem may be emotional. In that case, try this exercise.

Seated or lying comfortably, note where the restriction or obstruction is located. Clearly identify the place you feel it. Then:

  • How does it feel? Find a specific word or phrase that describes it. It could be an emotion word or a physical word.
  • Ask yourself what it looks like: what is its shape or color or size? Visualize it clearly.
  • Now, send your breath to the center of that sensation. Breathe into it.
  • Watch what happens as you breathe and pay attention.
  • Obstructions or restrictions that have an emotional basis will often disappear when you become aware of them, as long as you do not fight to push them away.
  • Ask yourself what it would take to make the block get smaller or disappear and imagine doing what it would take. Often breathing into the sensation and exhaling away from it will release the sensation.

Try this each time you feel the restriction when you practice.

My Breathing Plan

Being intentional about learning to use breath is important. Simply record your two-week plan here.

I plan to start practicing diaphragmatic breathing regularly on (date) _____.

I am going to keep track of practicing for a minute or two:

- ❑ Using a tally on a note card
- ❑ Using my phone or tablet app

I am going to remind myself to breathe:

- ❑ Using a task reminder on a device
- ❑ Using times when I have to wait

When I am ready to increase practice time:

- ❑ I will do it at this time _____
- ❑ I will use this phrase _____
- ❑ I will use this app _____
- ❑ I will add this music _____

After two weeks, I have learned:

_____
_____

I plan to continue awareness of breathing to manage stress by:

_____
_____
_____

Physically Relax

STEP #2
Physically Relax

Uptight. Does this describe you when stress hits? This description holds a world of truth about how it feels to be stressed out. The immediate result of the physical stress response is that your body prepares to move. Muscles contract, ready to spring into action. All people react to stress by tightening up physically. And they don't notice it until they have knots in their backs or headaches.

Physical relaxation does not come naturally if you are stressed out. What makes it worse is if you think you can be relaxed and also alert and "on the job." If you are not monitoring your tension level, you won't notice the following signs of tension until they hurt:

- tightened neck or shoulders muscles

- tight lower back, buttocks

- tense legs

- pain in jaw (even developing TMJ)

Tension headaches are born of tense muscles in the head and neck that restrict blood flow or affect nerves. If your job involves lots of thinking, you can get tight muscles around your skull, and that tightness contributes to headaches.

How could you be unaware of your need for physical relaxation? Are you using relaxation substitutes instead of physical relaxation? Lots of people don't believe they *can* relax or don't believe they *should* be physically relaxed while working at the job or around the house, and they wait to the end of the day to relax. Are you a person who ends the day by doing things you believe are relaxing but which also may have negative consequences, such as:

- Are you a "relax with dinner" or "relax by eating" person? (Not necessarily the same, except food is involved.) The obvious problem is eating may cause you to feel some relaxation in your attitude or mood, but it will not relax muscles that get you uptight, and it may increase your stress due to weight gain!

- ○ If your relaxation time is the evening meal, are you are trying to get the most out of the relaxation of eating, lingering over the meal or eating too much or feeling you need dessert to genuinely relax?

- ○ Are you someone who eats sweets or chips or snacks, hoping the eating-as-reward will relax you?

- Do you regularly relax after a busy day with a drink? Alcohol may be a very reliable way to start *feeling* loose, but is not always associated with muscle relaxation. Having a drink is a common and socially acceptable means of inducing a relaxed feeling. Relying on drinking to relieve stress runs the risk of developing health problems or even addiction.

  - ○ If one drink becomes two or three, especially before dinner, you may end up both drinking and then eating too much.

  - ○ If you have the drinks before bedtime to settle down, you will probably accomplish your goal to get drowsy, but won't sleep as well as the result of the alcohol.

- Other drugs. Are you joining the ranks of people who smoke marijuana to relax? You will find that this certainly makes you feel less stressed, but the many negative outcomes of using marijuana regularly may create other stressors. Do you use an anti-anxiety medication such as a benzodiazepine? This book of solutions is not intended to be primer on the perils of addiction to any substance, but think carefully about using drugs of any kind for the sole purpose of relaxation and evaluate the risks you may run if you do.

- Electronic relaxation comes in many forms. Do you watch television? Play video or electronic games for long stretches at the end of the day? Play computer games, even interactive games? These are so good at "zoning you out" that you may not realize they ultimately increase stress. The sensory bombardment of electronics can be over-stimulating for your nervous system, even though you are not using your body at all. With electronic relaxation, as with eating and drinking for stress relief, moderation is called for.

Relaxation Ideas

Look at your current habits. Ask, "What do I do now to relax?" Make a list:

Physical activities:

_____

_____

_____

_____

Eating: What types of foods, when, with or without others at a meal, etc.

_____

_____

_____

_____

Using alcohol, drugs or medications:

_____

_____

_____

_____

Electronic diversions:

_____

_____

_____

_____

Believe it or not, physical activities are better sources of physical relaxation than sitting still. A later chapter will discuss aerobic exercise specifically because it is a great long-term relaxer, but it does not help out at the moments when stress is high. Aerobic or anaerobic workouts are of great benefit to discharge pent-up energy and improve neurochemical changes associated with stress.

Some physical activities are just right for uptight muscles and immediate relaxation. These techniques help loosen tensed muscles, increase general blood-flow, and readjust tensed-up posture. These techniques can be done anywhere. Don't wait to get out of the car, out from behind the desk or off the computer in order to get some physical tension release.

Relax Anywhere!

Here are some (of the many) methods for immediate tension reduction, in addition to breathing, that do not require special instruction. The three things you can do anywhere are tense/release patterns, stretching, and posture change.

Muscle Tense and Relax

Practice the following simple muscle tense and release pattern:

- Working muscle groups from the top of your head down to your feet, tighten the muscle then relax abruptly. For example, tighten your face by frowning and pursing your lips. Then relax. Work your shoulders by hunching them upward and releasing. Make fists or curl your toes and then open them up. You will feel the blood flow warmly through your hands and feet. Pull in your stomach and let it go. Tighten your buttocks against the chair and relax. Except for making faces, no one in the office may even realize you are doing this.

- You will see that you were tighter than you realized. Try tensing and releasing three times to get the optimal release.

Stretching

Another series of relaxing moves includes stretching methods. Follow this simple, general rule about stretching for release: never do anything that hurts! If it hurts, stop immediately. Stretching is simply meant to release tension and thereby enhance blood flow, which results in muscle relaxation and feeling better. Several of these can be done while you are continuing with work and only require a momentary pause. These also be used when you move from one location to another. Try the following stretching techniques:

- Simply yawn, stretch your arms upward and release. Repeat.

- When you go to the bathroom, take the opportunity to stop and stretch briefly.

- Gentle leg lunges give you a stretch for legs that have been sitting too long or are too tight.

- For gentle back stretching, try torso relaxation. With feet comfortably spread apart for support, try letting your torso fall forward with the head gently leading the way down, bending at the waist, and coming back into an upright position by literally reversing the motion. Try imagining you are a puppet being released and then drawn upright by a string.

- Try continuing the action of this simple stretch into an overhead stretch once you are upright. Lift up your arms, reaching high overhead and gently tilt the head by lifting the chin until you gaze directly up. Make this and every release gentle, not sudden.

- Seated-at-desk head tilt: You can do this while on the phone, looking at the computer, etc., and not even lose time from work when you have that "allotted time" pressure. ***Do not rotate your neck in a circle!*** Let your ear fall toward your shoulder as far as it can without hurting. Raise your head upright. Then let your chin drop slowly to your chest and raise your head upright. Feel the stretch down your back. Then drop the other ear toward the other shoulder and, again, raise your head before letting your head feel heavy and drop slowly backward. Return to the upright position, just like the seat on an airplane, before you go on to repeat this.

- Seated-at-desk arm stretch: Raise one arm straight overhead, then bend it at the elbow, reaching with that hand down and toward the other side of your body, as if you were going to scratch your other shoulder blade. Then relax. Take the same arm and reach across your chest and wrap your hand around the opposite shoulder. Using the unoccupied hand, grasp the elbow of the reaching arm and gently exert pressure to increase the stretch in the shoulder and upper arm.

Practicing those stretches will help keep you loose when things could make you uptight.

Seated Posture Change

One other way to keep yourself from inadvertently tightening up is the seated posture change. This preventive measure can be practiced constantly if you have to sit at a desk. It involves regularly rotating through changed positions. Have a stool (or just a box) by your feet on which to rest them. For 15 minutes in each position, sit with one foot raised, then the other, then both, then neither. Use a back pillow or rolled towel, and put it behind lower back, then middle back, then do without it.

Stay Hydrated

Progressive relaxation, stretching, and posture changes are the simple techniques for relaxation which can be done at work (without being obvious) or at home. But to be at our best and most relaxed, we should also watch out for the tendency to drink caffeinated beverages. Most of us tend to go for the tea, coffee or soda, and we do not drink enough water. And, if you have no other opportunities to get muscle relaxation at the moment, try relaxing from the inside out by using an opportunity to drink a cup of something warm at your work station to warm your inner self.

- Keep a glass of water nearby so you do not have to think about going to get a drink when you are thirsty. Rather, drink before you get thirsty.

- Drink a warm, non-stimulating beverage such as bouillon or herbal tea, and focus on the sensations. Many herbal teas such as chamomile have relaxing properties.

2-Minute Relaxers

You may have a work life that does not allow many chances to relax, but anyone can take a minute or two to do this. Many people now have on their wrist device or handheld device a 90- minute reminder to move, especially if they are stuck at desks all day. You can move your body in many brief but creative ways, from simply taking the stairs instead of an elevator or walking up and down a hallway, to:

- Office yoga   • 2-minute workout   • Office recess

Guides to do these can be found on several locations on the internet, whether from websites or on YouTube.

But if you have an active job, your relaxation might be better done with peaceful and physical quiet:

- Look at pictures of your loved ones or a recent vacation (I would suggest being careful about Facebooking during this time unless you are impervious to Facebook envy.).

- Close your eyes and do a brief meditation using any of several guided imagery apps.

- Use a device or an app for a few minutes of physical/mental calming such as Emwave from Heartmath™ or Wild Divine from Deepak Chopra or Muse or any of several similar device.

- Do some mindful coloring (adult coloring books are currently being utilized to engage in stress reduction).

- Tend plants in your work or home space.

Longer-term Outcomes

Many years ago, Herbert Benson studied meditation for its benefits of deep relaxation and discovered the health benefits of deliberately relaxing your body on a daily basis. For your total benefit, you should consider learning a method or system of relaxation that provides the deep relaxation good for high blood pressure, heart health, and emotional calm.

Today there are many paths to achieve this state via progressive muscle relaxation using stretching, tense-and-release or imagery. Such techniques may require some instruction and there are terrific resources online and via YouTube to teach or demonstrate effective ways to do it. Whatever version you choose, when you achieve that deep sense of relaxation, take some diaphragmatic breaths and notice the physical sensation of relaxation. When you pair relaxation with breathing often enough, you will be able to cue the state of relaxation with a breath—a very handy ability to reduce stress in the moment!

Many people who are stressed do not recognize in themselves the subtle or not-so-subtle ways they resist making the time and space in their schedules to do the briefest of relaxation methods. I asked one tense client to listen to a guided imagery to help him relax before sleep, and when he told me he had not done it quite the way I asked, I got curious and asked him, "What do you mean?" and he replied without any hint of objection, "Well, I started, but I could tell what they were getting at, so I just turned it off. I already knew what they intended me to do." The intention was that he would listen all the way through and relax, a state he did not achieve just by knowing how it would occur. Most people don't relax just by thinking that they should. This client and I had some work to do before he was going to relax!

There are many places to learn relaxation techniques: take yoga or meditation classes, get a massage on a regular basis, or take courses in relaxation offered by community colleges. You might want to study martial arts, which contain strong components of relaxation. Some apps that have good options, although you should choose the voice and style you like, to learn relaxation are:

- Simply Being

- Calm

- www.healthjourneys.com is an excellent source of these meditations

- I have a download with two versions of muscle relaxation available through my website, www.margaretwehrenberg.com

Everyone should have a means of physical release, and it might take time to explore what method or discipline works for you. Working with a person who can teach you yoga, meditation or relaxation of any kind requires you to schedule the time, and an instructor can help you explore any resistance or reluctance you may have about changing your current ways of handling stress.

Commit to Yourself

However done, discipline and practice in your relaxation method makes it easier to induce a state of relaxation instantaneously under stress. Make a commitment to yourself here. It helps to keep to the commitment if you observe benefits and get some outside advice when you encounter any impediments to your practice.

Relaxation methods I will try at work:

_____

_____

_____

_____

_____

After 7 days, benefits I can see:

_____

_____

_____

_____

_____

Relaxation methods I will try at home:

_____

_____

_____

_____

_____

_____

After 7 days, benefits I can see:

_____

_____

_____

_____

_____

_____

Obstacles I have encountered and sources of help to work them out:

_____

_____

_____

_____

_____

_____

_____

_____

_____

_____

My plans to learn more about physical relaxation:

_____

_____

_____

_____

_____

_____

_____

_____

_____

The following are scripts to lead you through typical progressive muscle relaxation using the "tense-and-release" muscle relaxation method and also the "image of light" for guided imagery. You may want someone to read these to you.

SCRIPT

Tense and Release

1. Make sure you are in a relaxed position, e.g., sitting upright or lying flat.

2. Begin the progressive muscle relaxation exercise by closing your eyes and then allowing your focus to rest entirely on the sensations of each muscle group as you move through them.

3. Begin at head or at feet, and now go to each muscle group following the point at which you start.

4. Tense, hold, and then relax. If starting at the feet:

   a. "Tense your toes, curl them tight, tight, tight. Now release. Feel the warmth flood into them. Feel the energy and warmth suffuse those muscles. With each exhalation, the warmth flows into your toes." (3 times)

   b. Follow up the body, suggesting tense- hold-release for each muscle group.

   c. If going up from the toes, end with the energy flowing in with each breath and now coursing down through the body with each exhalation.

5. If starting at the head, the order of group could be: scalp, forehead, face, neck (no circles, but let head lean forward or bend with the weight of the head pulling the head along), shoulders, upper arms, forearm and wrist, fingers, chest, back, buttocks, thighs, shin, calf, ankle and foot. If going top-down, keep adding the sense of energy flowing down through the relaxed muscles, and end with the awareness of the soles of the feet feeling connected to the earth through the floor.

Image of Light

This classic visualization—Image of Light—is a well-known imagery for relaxation:

1. Imagine that there is above your head a sphere of light/energy.

2. The light is the color you most associate with (peace, calm, healing, energy, etc.)

3. As you inhale you draw it into body through breath or through crown chakra.

4. As you exhale the flow of energy streams through body. The physical experience of warmth and vibrant energy relaxes each part of the body as the breath is exhaled downward from the top of the head through each part of the body, one breath at a time.

5. It may connect through the spine as roots into the earth.

6. It may connect through the soles of feet.

7. As your body fills with energy, it exudes through every pore, forming an envelope of energy around the body.

8. Find a word that associates the sensation of total relaxation, such as calm, or even a sound such as 'ah' or 'mmm.'

9. This energy is impervious to negativity, any experience of which is simply reflected away. And it is completely permeable for all positive experiences, which can be taken in completely.

10. As the envelope of energy fades through the day it can be renewed with deep breath, imaging light, and saying or hearing the sound you chose.

STEP # 3

Be Assertive

Be Assertive

Assertiveness is an attitude. This is not to say that you should go around "with an attitude," as we describe people who are always on the offense. The assertive attitude is never a noticeable thing you put on. The assertive attitude is your stance in the world; you assume that you are as valuable as every other person in your life. When you are assertive, you approach the world with the attitude that your needs deserve to be met as much as anyone's and you are willing to personally assure that those needs are met.

You are as valuable as everyone else

Negative stress results when people believe it is their responsibility to make sure others are taken care of before they meet their own needs. Unassertive people will meet family demands and work demands, and then try to take care of their own needs when there is time. Maybe. Mostly, unassertive people end up stressed out because there never comes a day when other people have no demands. There is never a day when people who have become used to being taken care of suddenly leave the unassertive person alone, and, even if they did, that person is too out of practice when it comes to self-care.

You are probably thinking, "Of course my needs are important!" Do you think you will get to watch your show as soon as everyone is settled? Do you think you will get to your homework after your friend has finished talking to you? Do you plan to do your own work as soon as your family is taken care of for the night, or when they are away for the weekend? Are you the person at work who says to your colleagues when they are leaving for lunch, "You go ahead, I'll eat as soon as I get through this list of phone calls (or as soon as I finish this job, or when everyone else has a break)." If these examples sound like you, you may not be assertive enough to avoid the impact of stress. An attitude readjustment is necessary!

When you are appropriately assertive, you can see how you are valuable to everyone around you. Your co-workers need you. If you are the cashier at the local Wal-Mart, your team depends on you showing up for work just as much as if you are a mom who is at home caring for a sick child. If you are a medical doctor, your patients depend on seeing you, just as if you are a car mechanic repairing the cars people need to get to work or to the doctor. You are needed if you are the maintenance staff just as much as if you are an office manager scheduled to lead meetings all day. Knowing that what you do is important to others will lead you to take good care of yourself and to assertively protect your energy. One man I knew was on maintenance staff at a hospital and he told me he knew he was valuable to the work of every employee and the health of every patient. Without his work to provide a clean and smoothly operating environment the healing work of the hospital could not be done well.

Add yourself to your priorities!

The belief that you are important does not mean that no one else is important. It does not mean that you should suddenly become selfish and refuse to take care of the tasks or responsibilities you believe are yours to do. It just means that you will add yourself to your list of priorities. Life puts a lot of demands on your time. You want to meet those demands without suffering from too much stress. Keep stress at bay by making few demands on yourself. Taking care of your needs is as important as meeting the demands of the other important people in your life. Keeping stress at bay also means that any demand you meet will not be destructive to your well-being. Why would you agree to destructive demands? It is too easy!

- Do you demand of yourself to go to every single traveling soccer game in which your child plays? Do you believe that is important? What if that schedule causes you to skip your own exercise? This would be detrimental to your well-being.

- Do you meet a demand to stay up late at night so that you can finish the office work, email, the housework or schoolwork, but then suffer exhaustion? You will feel more stress than doing the work at a more reasonable pace.

Hurting yourself to meet other people's wishes is self-destructive. If someone else wants you to do any kind of work or do any kind of favor, no matter how reasonable the request is on the face of it, ask yourself, "What will doing this cost me in time, money, energy or, most especially, in terms of a lost opportunity to take care of myself?"

If you value yourself and are assertive enough, you can prevent the stress of managing the demands of others from taking too big a toll. What are the guidelines?

- Limit work each day to a specific, reasonable number of hours.

- Keep to your own healthy habits, such as daily exercise, meditation, stretching, regular meals, or quiet time.

- Always ask yourself what an unexpected demand will change in your schedule before you say yes.

Managing stress means that you will *balance* your needs with others' needs. That is appropriate assertiveness.

Everyone gets the same number of hours in a day

Meeting a Spiritual Expectation

What if you feel a spiritual or philosophical obligation to be giving to others? Are you guided by a value of selflessness? Do you feel dedicated to some goal? Do you believe you should devote 100% of your energy to the things that are important: to you, your children or spouse, your friends, your church, your charity? You may want to be a person who is unselfish and who values being a giver, and this is a terrific value.

So think about what this really means in your life. Giving of your time, talent, energy, and resources is a good thing. It is also true that a well that is never replenished by another source of water eventually runs dry. Look at your giving and see if you are a well running dry without water left for the thirsty souls who need a drink. You may want to be giving to others, but if you have given all your energy away and have nothing left to give, what good will you be? That question may sound selfish, but is really based on the principle that *a well-nurtured soul has more to give than a depleted one.*

Giving does not equal lack of assertiveness, but if you are not assertive, you suffer more from this type of demand-meeting stress than people who put themselves first on their priority list. You will suffer exhaustion or over-stimulation when you give too much time, attention, energy, problem solving, or emotions to others, without considering your own level of energy. If you are a giver in this life, you must have ways to replenish your energy or you will run out of resources to give to those who have come to rely on you. Appropriate assertiveness will help you maintain the personal energy to help others.

Self-Care Plan

Do you know what you need in order to continue giving to others? What sources replenish your energy, your attention, your emotional strength?

List the things that you are *currently doing* that make you feel rested, energetic and available to others:

Daily activities_____

_____

_____

Weekly activities: _____

_____

_____

Occasional activities: _____

_____

_____

Commit: For one week I will do the following things to take good care of myself:

❑ Daily   ❑ Weekly   ❑ Occasionally

Note to self upon completion of that activity: Worth repeating?

_____

_____

_____

_____

Assertiveness at Work

Assertiveness looks different at work than at home. It looks different than assertiveness with friends or in social groups. It's usually easier to spot assertiveness problems in the workplace. Take a look at your style in your work.

- Do you know when to tell a supervisor your workload is too full or when to adjust a deadline that cannot be met?

- Do you worry whether you will lose your job if you say you have hit your limit of hours worked or tasks assigned? Work will stress you out when you make too many assumptions about what is expected of you without checking them out.

- Do you feel intense time pressure for job completion?

- Do you get too many demands for your attention at once? That can stress you out. If you cannot control the pace of your work, such as in the work of assembly lines, nurses, cashiers, or air traffic controllers, you are the most vulnerable to stress of any working group.

- Do you know what your priorities are at all times? Another form of work pressure is having too many assigned duties or specific tasks but you cannot tell which is most important or you cannot be the one who decides what to do first.

To relieve these kinds of stress, appropriate work assertiveness will help. You can learn this kind of assertiveness if you practice a couple of simple skills that will help you to relax at work:

Use the urgent-important matrix to make priority decisions. If you are in the type of job that has a variable pace when work might suddenly intensify, you will reduce the stress of that increased demand on you by thinking and planning ahead of time about what matters most. Then assertively create a priority list in your mind, in the computer or on paper, and follow it. One of the most useful ways to do this is to categorize each task according to the matrix credited to General Eisenhower's statement that many things that are urgent are not important and many things that are important are not urgent.

Urgent - Important Matrix

Urgent & Important	Not Urgent & Important

Urgent & Not Important	Neither Urgent nor Important

There are a couple of terrific apps that are paired with a second app that helps you keep time for these:

- Focus Matrix

- Eisenhower app (found on www.eisenhower.me along with excellent time management information)

Ask about quality of acceptable work, or when is your work product 'good enough'? Another form of work assertiveness comes in when you consult with a supervisor or the peers who work with you on the job about what an acceptable level of quality is for your work. For example, if you have a perfectionistic streak, you may be working too hard at getting the quality of the job just right when it is more important to finish it well enough but not perfectly. There is a guiding principle call the Pareto Principle which indicates you will be best off when you can identify and determine which factors are most important and should receive the most attention, based on an efficient use of your resources. If you are spending too much time and effort on work activities that do not sufficiently move you toward task completion or correct completion, shift to those activities that will give you most of the result and get those done first. You may then get a job done well enough. That 80/20 rule applies to most of life's activities.

What if your job seems to have no in-between on quality? If you are a nurse or an engineer or in other kinds of situations where "good enough" is harder to define, plan stress-managing tools to diminish stress caused by a rapid pace with high quality demand, and then be assertive enough to follow through. For example, you will improve your performance and keep your stress level manageable by taking breaks and lunches. Every study done on this issue shows the harm of working straight through a shift or straight through to finish work. The cost of not taking breaks is lower work performance and may also be your well-being. Believing this and sticking to it requires assertiveness, especially in jobs such as nursing, in which the work is clearly important to others and when you feel guilty if you take a break when someone needs your attention.

- Research shows that people work more productively and with fewer accidents when they take scheduled breaks, so that they get more done in work time than if they worked straight through the break. Be assertive *with yourself.* Ask yourself whether it is true for you, as it is for most people, that you do better when you take regular breaks. Establish and keep to a work schedule that makes you productive.

- Learn the difference between an emergency and a situation you expect and know is going to be difficult. Learn the difference between urgent and important. Many urgent requests are not important, they just come with a timetable.

> # Learn the difference between urgency and emergency

- Discuss with your manager ahead of time about the expectations that apply to these urgent situations. Ask when you would be expected to skip your breaks or otherwise go above and beyond the job description in order to be regarded as cooperative and energetic: two desirable traits in a worker. Appropriate assertiveness will help you to recognize you are not required to give up every break and every lunch in order to be seen as cooperative.

- Count the cost to yourself of giving in to the pace and cheating yourself out of stress relievers.

- Observe when you feel invigorated because the stress is challenging.

Guidelines to become more assertive at work by handling time frames:

Ask what the time frame is. Do not assume that it must be immediate or sooner! Many people simply forget to ask. When you begin to do this, your stress will immediately lessen because you will be clear about your boss's demand for completion of the work. When you make assumptions because you are afraid to ask, they may well be incorrect assumptions. Asking does not equal refusing a task. You can ask a manger, "I want to do this as you expect, so when you need this to be done? Should it have higher priority than this other task I am working on?" The less you assume about what others expect, the less stress you will feel, because you will know when to rise to the occasion and when you can work at a pace that won't stress you out.

Ask about other people's time frames to remind you to consider your own time frames. You may well have more than one project and more than one person expecting your work product. Is this a customer who needs the work by noon or one that won't be back for the work until Tuesday? What do you already have on your time frame when a new job comes in?

Learn to prioritize. Prioritizing is a challenge for unassertive people. When the time frame interferes with another project, say so without complaining or without assuming what your clients or your boss will decide about it. It is less stressful to let someone else think about their priorities before you try to accommodate them. When it is your boss assigning a new project, let the boss set the priority. As they say, "That's why she gets the big bucks." An appropriately assertive comment would sound like this. "You asked me to type the report on the Smith project, and I am not done yet. Do you want me to set that aside to do this first?" Or, "Our team is working on the numbers for the Jones estimate. Does this new assignment get priority over that?" You can ask about priorities no matter what your job position is. Managing your job stress means understanding priorities whether you are a receptionist who needs to know when the filing is more important than the copying or you are a department head needing to know which budget restrictions have priority.

Be willing to use your own judgment. Asking for clear information does not mean your boss will be clear about answering, but when you are clear about what you need to know, you will know if you have received a clear answer. If not, you can diminish stress by planning a course of action to cope with that dilemma. Brainstorm first, and then choose the best option to meet your needs as well as the demands of the task. For right now, ask yourself, "What expectations do I need to clarify at work?" List them on the next page with the name of the person who might help you to make that clarification.

Expectations of Me:	Who Expects It?

Brainstorming a Problem

First, find a co-worker, friend or family member who can help brainstorm about your problem without telling you what to do. Then, together, get out some paper and answer these questions:

1. What is my problem? Be specific!

_____

_____

_____

_____

_____

_____

_____

_____

2. What are ideal outcomes? If it all goes well, what will happen?

_____

_____

_____

_____

_____

_____

_____

_____

3. What options do I have? (List every possibility no matter how silly it may sound. You are not yet making a decision, just listing. List all options, even those you would never choose, such as "I could quit work and move to Alaska," as well as more reasonable options such as, "I could have a serious conversation with my boss."

Option A:_____

_____

_____

_____

_____

_____

Option B:_____

_____

_____

_____

_____

_____

Option C: _____

_____

_____

_____

_____

_____

4. Now, evaluate the options. On paper, make two columns titled "Pros" and "Cons" and for each and every option list how it would help and how it could hurt to follow that course of action. Doing this for all options can make you feel more in control immediately.

Option A:

Pros	Cons

Option B:

Pros	Cons

Option C:

Pros	Cons

5. Choose the most helpful option that has the most acceptable risk (more pros than cons) and decide very specifically when you will act on it.

_____

_____

_____

_____

_____

_____

Action Plan

Take action! After you pick which option looks most likely to get you your ideal outcome, then you are ready to make a plan. Write out the steps that you must take to complete your option and give each step a time frame. For example, if your action plan requires something like asking for a meeting, you have at least two dates of action: the day to request and the day to meet.

Step 1. (Complete by _____)

_____

_____

_____

Step 2. (Complete by _____)

_____

_____

_____

Step 3. (Complete by _____)

_____

_____

_____

Step 4. (Complete by _____)

_____

_____

_____

Follow the course you decide on. Do not delay once you decide the date you want to make your move. The action plan is not complete until all the steps have been taken.

Evaluate your actions once they are done. Knowing whether your assertiveness brought good results will encourage you to be more assertive in the future. Paying attention to what happens when you take action is the surest way to learn to take more action and more effective action to reduce negative stress.

How did this go?

_____

_____

_____

_____

_____

_____

_____

_____

_____

_____

_____

_____

_____

_____

_____

_____

_____

Assertiveness with Yourself

What if you are your own boss? Not only do you fall prey to the idea that you never need a break, a lunch (without a meeting while you eat) or a set time to leave for the day, but you are the only one who can decide to set up a work pace for yourself. Also, whether you own your own business or you are a manager who can set your own deadlines or organize projects, you are the one who makes the work demands on yourself. Alas, this does not mean you have reasonable time expectations or clear priorities. To whom will you go to ask, "How soon must the work be done?" or "Which work is more important?"

Have a Meeting With Yourself

You must have a meeting with yourself, and it would be a good idea to have someone listen to you while you reason with yourself, who will point out any flaws in your analysis about the importance of the work.

People who are self-employed rarely have administrative meetings with themselves, but it's a good idea. Having a business plan is as important for an individual as it is for a large company. If you have not done this yet or if you have not reviewed your plan in a long time, you may be creating unnecessary stress from having ill-defined or contradictory goals. You may be the person who as a volunteer who coordinates a community project, you may do crafts to sell online, you may be a clergy person, an accountant or a therapist in private practice. In any of these kinds of roles, you should examine your work load and your work style with your self-care and time management in mind.

Whenever your say "yes" to more work or set a deadline for work in progress, evaluate how it meshes with other work already in progress. Then very seriously ask yourself, "How important is it?" Is repairing that carburetor really so important that it should be done before you finish invoicing or sending the bills? Should you spend time designing the product information summary before you make the cold calls that will result in appointments for which you need the flyer?

Being assertive with yourself is a challenging task. Try:

1. Developing a business plan, at least to the extent that you have clearly defined work goals. These include goals for production of work or money as well as goals for time you will spend on aspects of the business. This is a multi-step task and there are books available to help if you need help with this.

2. Finding others who do similar work to meet with regularly to discuss aspects of conducting business.

3. Finding someone who can encourage your efforts to set priorities. Make sure you choose someone who is not affected by your priorities. Consider the problem of choosing someone who has a personal agenda, like a spouse, who advises you to prioritize his dinner over your sales call! That example would rank as pretty obvious interference, but other people's agendas are not always so obvious and when they conflict with what is right for you, it is stressful.

4. Set priorities for work, separate from other demands. Also set family priorities, then those of volunteer groups and friends. Self-employed people are often stressed out by the conflict between work and family, but it prioritizing work and family is done by everyone who needs their income or can't afford to lose their job. Prioritizing both sets of demands makes choices clearer. With each list clear, you can then mesh them. Family needs do sometimes come before work tasks, but you cannot know when to defer to a family activity without knowing the relative importance of each activity. It may be much more important to see the championship game your daughter is playing in than it is to take a phone call from a client on a matter that could wait until the next day. The call is important but the game is urgent and important.

5. Put your priorities in writing. It will help you take this seriously. You will more clearly see the results of your decisions and hold yourself to them better than if you just think about them.

6. Develop a time management scheme that works for you. There are many resources available in books and on websites for time management such as apps that use the Eisenhower (urgent/important) matrix or electronic calendars for iOS or Google or Microsoft that offer task reminders and time reminders.

Work Demands

To begin, choose which of the previous steps you will follow and list those steps you want to make to clarify your work demands:

1. _____
   _____
   _____
   _____

2. _____
   _____
   _____
   _____

3. _____
   _____
   _____
   _____

4. _____
   _____
   _____
   _____

Assertiveness at Home

Do you have trouble with assertiveness in your home? Do you know what it would look like? An assertive attitude is tough to find and maintain for parents raising their children and making a home. It is even rougher on dads and moms who come home from work to the work of raising the children. One big problem for parents is saying "no" to demands from their children that are reasonable but not necessary. It is hard to figure out when to say "no" to that reasonable demand in order to keep your stress at a manageable level. What if the kids want to go shopping or make cookies or want a ride to a friend's house or have a friend overnight? None of those activities deserve a "no" because there is something wrong or unnecessary about them. But you should say "no" if you have higher priorities for your time.

> # Just because they ask,
> # you don't have to say yes

Problems in parenting and the right answers to fix them can fill volumes, but for the purposes of stress management, there is one cardinal rule: *"Just because they ask, you don't have to say yes."* Asking does not mean that you have to give it to them now or in the way they ask for it. To manage parental stress you are allowed to say "no." You may say it unequivocally. You can say "later" and you can identify what later is: 15 minutes, 1 hour, tomorrow, etc. You can say, "I will give you some of what you want," e.g., "I can give you a ride home, but I cannot take you there. Is there someone else who can drive?" Remember the following ideas when dealing with the demands your children make on you:

1. You can listen to requests respectfully and all the way through without being obligated to say "yes" at the end of the request.

2. You can say "no" to children and not hurt them forever. In fact, it is really good for them. How else do kids learn to tolerate frustration and avoid becoming totally self-absorbed? They need to know you also have needs that deserve respect.

3. Children also need to learn to say "no" for their own protection. To say "no" to their own impulsivity, to say "no" to friends who entice them to do wrong actions, to say "no" to using drugs or having sex inappropriately. They **need** you to role-model such assertiveness so **they** can learn to do it in their lives.

The same rules apply to extended family. You may not have children of your own, but you may still have extended family members who want your help. They present other types of family demands, but may still require a "no" from you. You can say "no" to your mother and not hurt her forever. You said it a lot when you were two, and she is still there. If your mother wants you to fix her faucet, you can pick the day that works best for you. If your sister needs your help to babysit for her kids, you can decide if you have time without stress. They are her kids and her responsibility.

Remember that demands often intrude into the house from family and friends via texts and other messages that can now come via so many sources. You can say "no" to any type of incoming alert or message, a text, a message via Facebook or even an old-fashioned phone call. Just because it can be answered, does not mean you must answer with a "yes." If it has a notification signal, you can turn it off. If it sends you mail, you can look at it later. Instantaneous communication has created a challenge because it changes too rapidly to develop social rules that are recognized universally. Do you have to read and answer every communication immediately? Some people hold their phones 24/7 and expect you will too. Some people think it is reasonable for all family members to be using devices while sitting at a meal together and others regard that as the height of rudeness. You have to set your own rules to manage your stress.

Making a change is tough. You will have to evaluate the demands in your life from your family and make some choices about what is important. Decide what you want to do and prioritize those things so you know what you can do. Decide what you want to say "no" to. Start getting a grip by surveying demands on your time:

- Think over the number of extracurricular activities your children are in that demand your time and attention.

- Think over the number of social obligations of the family.

- Think over the sources of electronic demands for your attention and how you want to curtail them.

- Review the demands for help from extended family. It might be very useful for you to talk this over with people who are uninvolved in your family so that you can get an unbiased perspective on what is necessary.

When you are starting to say "no," it won't be easy to make a change. Your family and friends won't be expecting it or won't take you seriously. There is a simple action step to get around that problem. When you decide to start saying "no" practice saying, "I'll think that over," or "Let me get back to you," or "Give me a minute to think about that," for EVERY SINGLE request made to you, regardless of how much you want to say "yes," until you get the hang of saying "no."

Let Me Think About It

List situations in which you will practice saying, "Let me think about it."

_____

_____

_____

_____

_____

_____

_____

_____

_____

_____

_____

_____

_____

_____

_____

_____

_____

_____

_____

_____

STEP #4

Manage Noise

STEP #4
Manage Noise

Create Quiet Zones

The most insidious of all stressors is uninterrupted noise. You can suffer this at work or at home and may not even realize the impact of noise on your nerves. Continuous electronic noise is a major contributor to this kind of stress. The sources of this are many. Fans, furnaces, fluorescent lights, computers, and all types of white noise challenge your nervous system. Notification signals from texts, emails, instant messaging of various kinds and, yes, even phone calls, pepper us with demands to pay attention all day long. Other types of electronic sound come in supposedly pleasing packages: every store you go into, every elevator you ride in, every restaurant, every waiting room you sit in, and now even gas pumps play some type of music. Whenever you are in a car or at home, you or your family may have radio, music or TV going. Especially in urban environments, the unabating sounds of the street: cars, trucks, trains, etc., are stressful.

Noise has a profound impact on your senses even if you habituate to it. When you first enter an environment you will notice the sounds, but eventually you get accustomed to the presence of the sound so you can place your attention on other aspects of the situation. Noise is not relaxing if you have not chosen it and even if you are not consciously listening to it. When it is background to the important things that require your attention, it causes your brain to work overtime filtering it out of your direct attention, especially when your work is done in an environment with noise or continual talking as would be the case in an office full of cubicles. Your brain registers the sensory impact, even when you are not paying attention to it. Especially if you work a job in which noise must be attended to, as when changes in mechanical sounds are important to diagnosing a problem in an engine, your brain needs a rest from that impact of background noise.

You may try to create an inner environment wearing your headset and listening to words or music. Music you choose to hear may be helpful rather than disruptive like the noise (or music) you do not choose. Music that does not pull at your attention or distract you may promote focus. It may create a positive background to help you sleep, work in a 'cube' environment or live in a communal setting such as a dormitory. There are also situations when music you choose may work to counterbalance disturbing background noises, or the music may override mild unpredictable interferences like voices in another office or traffic. The right volume level of non-distracting music may actually enhance your focus in those environments.

Be aware that when you must filter or block out background noise/music, even if it boosts your focus to do so, you will pay a price of mental energy and you may be tired even if less disturbed by the noise in the environment. On the next worksheet you will identify sources of noise in your environment, and when you have noted the sources, you will need to consider your options to mitigate or eliminate those annoying, stressful noises. Among those options are:

1. Take a break. Especially from the noise from fans or lighting. You may not be able to escape them when you are at your work. You may only be able to get breaks from this type of noise. Try to plan breaks where the sounds are not continuous or at least where they are different. Noise cancellation headphones might provide a good option in an especially "humming" environment, especially if you add the option of pleasing music.

2. Get outside. Try to get outside and away from electronic noises to give your senses a break.

3. Get rid of it. Find out if you can eliminate radio or music at your worksite for all or part of the day. If it is not possible, identify whether variety is possible or if there is volume control available to you. Most of the time variably changing the type is better than no change at all.

4. Turn off the news or electronic entertainment at dinnertime. Even if your family objects, family life demands time to develop conversation and interest in each other. TV programs or other forms of distraction interfere with developing conversation or meaningful interaction that will emerge

from spending time together. TV often fills uncomfortable voids between people, but being together without electronic diversion creates the space in which conversation or interest in each other can emerge.

5. Even when you are alone, do not turn on music or programs unless you are deliberately listening to them. Having background noise can be grueling without your realizing it.

If you can become adept at managing noise, people will wonder why your environment is so soothing to be in and will never notice the absence of background noise that makes everything around you calmer.

Limiting Noise

Over the next few days, list every source of noise in your environment, whether you choose to have it there or not, and then identify those sources of noise that are not of your choosing and those that you choose:

_____

_____

_____

_____

_____

_____

_____

_____

_____

What can you do in your home or at your job to reduce your exposure to those noises or eliminate the noise altogether?

_____

_____

_____

_____

_____

_____

_____

_____

STEP #5

Wait

Wait

Use Waiting to Your Advantage

Waiting is boring. In the army they say boredom is the worst problem soldiers face. They are always told to "Hurry up!" and then "Wait!" Boredom is painful. Can you remember the last time you felt truly bored and how desperately you wanted to change that? There is no doubt that our many options for filling ears and eyes with engaging activity has changed the problem of boredom while waiting, but that does not mean you are using waiting to your advantage. Many kinds of waiting cannot be managed just by plugging in our headphones.

Think about the experiences you face every day that create stress for you because you have to wait:

- Are you on hold for half an hour with your insurance company waiting to find out why they have not sent you a claim check?

- Have you completed your part of the work and now you are waiting for the work someone else had to complete before you can turn the project in?

- Are you waiting for guests to arrive for the dinner you rushed to prepare?

- Are you in line at the hardware store when the connection to the internet goes down and you cannot get a receipt?

- Are you waiting for kids to come home and it is after curfew?

- Are you a student kept waiting on the professor's whim to get information you need for class?

- Are you waiting for a customer to make up his mind if he is going to buy from you or not?

- Are you waiting for your boss to finish that phone call so you can ask an important question before proceeding with the work?

- Are you waiting to find out the results of a job interview? Medical test? Pregnancy test?

There are all kinds of waiting. The kinds that last for minutes and the kinds that last for hours, days, and months. Waiting of any kind has one thing in common with all other kinds of waiting: No one likes to wait. Waiting is inherently stressful. Most people have trouble waiting without feeling anxious. How you handle waiting will solve stress before it happens.

Waiting for Brief Periods — Minutes at a Time

Here are some attitudes that help you handle the little waiting times and, in fact, turn them to your advantage:

1. Eagerly await waiting! Look forward to chances to wait. This attitude then greets waiting with a sigh of delight rather than a groan. You will make this realistic if you resolve to use your waiting for your benefit. Decide today to look for ways to wait productively.

2. Make waiting on the phone work for you. There are many times we have to wait on hold to get some personal or work-related business done. Instead of stressing out over waiting, have an idea of little things you can do that will productively use the little periods of waiting. There are many things you can do at your desk while waiting on the phone. Straighten papers, open envelopes or clean out the old dried up pens. File things. Clean out computer files. Water the plants. Enter new addresses or phone numbers in your contact list. Having headsets for phones, or using speakerphone, makes this even easier. Before you make a call you could get stuck on, get what you need to keep your hands busy while you wait. This works at home too. Don't make phone calls until you have a task at hand you can manage while waiting: knit, do laundry, dust, wash dishes, and so on.

3. Use brief waiting times to your mental or spiritual advantage. Make it a relief to wait.

4. Take the time to breathe deeply.

5. Try using the wait to make affirmations. (See Step 9 on Affirmations)

6. Consider how you feel physically: become mindful of yourself in your present setting. That's all. Mindfulness is restful and a major calming mental position. (Step 9 will discuss mindfulness.) This can result in great attentiveness to what comes next, and may be deeply relaxing.

7. In the same vein, try going blank mentally. (Just be sure that if you are on the phone you remember for whom you were waiting.)

8. Pray. Many people find that the relief of spiritual awareness through prayer makes them look forward to having the break of waiting.

Waiting Ideas

Make a list of short items you could use to fill minutes of waiting and decide where to keep it:

- _____
  _____

- _____
  _____

- _____
  _____

- _____
  _____

- _____
  _____

- _____
  _____

- _____
  _____

Waiting for a Longer Period—Hours at a Time

Intermediate periods of waiting, such as hours or a day, require a little more creativity. These also require a decision about what works for you to discharge the annoyance of waiting.

1. Plan ahead about small projects that you want to do when you have a little time. Make a list of those for work and for home, list the estimated time for the tasks, and keep it handy. You will be pleased with your productivity, and may even forget that waiting drives you crazy! This project list will include things like:

   a. sorting through a disorganized storage area

   b. cleaning out a file drawer

   c. sorting photos in your computer or phone

   d. making phone calls that are on the low priority list

   e. keeping your resume up-to-date

   f. replacing a switch on a broken lamp

   g. straightening garage shelves

   h. writing a birthday card to your sister

   i. calling your mother

   j. getting children's toys sorted out

   k. putting away the out-of-season clothes

2. Plan the kind of relaxation you always said you would do if you had a little time: read a book, watch a movie, do a woodworking project, clean your golf clubs, weed the garden, give yourself a pedicure, go to the park with the kids, call those health clubs to see about joining up, read new recipes, stare out the window, etc.

3. Get together with friends you don't see enough, even if it is for a cup of coffee or walk around the neighborhood. This can be very diverting and build relationships that may be suffering the impact of too little time and too much to do.

List Making

Do some serious list-making. Walk around the house and write down ideas. Every time you think, "If only I had time, I would . . . ," write down what you would do. Keep this list in your phone or tablet, or even keep it on paper. (You might try putting it into your newly acquired urgent-important matrix!) Get started here, and translate the results to a list you carry with you or put up in a visible place.

What do I want to do around the house?

_____

_____

_____

_____

_____

_____

_____

_____

Make a separate list for work in the same way.

_____

_____

_____

_____

_____

_____

_____

Waiting for Long Periods—
Days, Weeks or Months

Longer periods of waiting, such as when you must wait weeks or months for an outcome, pose a greater challenge. Common but uncomfortable kinds of waiting:

1. Waiting at work. Often there are wait periods when you cannot really do much to affect outcomes, like waiting to see if your job will be downsized, waiting when your boss retires to see if you will like the new boss or go job hunting, waiting while you are changing jobs. You want to stay involved where you are at the same time you are hoping to leave, or waiting to see if you will be accepted by colleagues at the new work site.

2. Waiting to have a baby. Another familiar waiting is the waiting couples go through to become pregnant or go through pregnancy, or waiting on an adoption. Especially when couples are going through infertility procedures, the up and down anticipation creates a peculiar twist on the nature of the wait.

3. Waiting for the outcome of medical tests and treatments. This is a harrowing kind of waiting because people are so often fearful of the outcomes, so waiting stress is increased by the life-changing or life-threatening nature of the outcome.

4. Waiting for results: Various board tests and applications have very long wait periods of many days or even weeks. Tests for medical boards or law boards. Applications to universities and graduate schools. Even job applications can have long waits.

Any particular day during these kinds of waits may require a combination of the tactics but, in particular, this kind of waiting requires an *attitude* about life that prepares you to avoid stress. This attitude develops as the result of:

1. Actively thinking about waiting as growing time. Possibilities and opportunities grow and develop while we are waiting for things. When you sense impatience churning, breathe and think to yourself that something is developing and you will see what it is when it breaks

through. The image of a bulb growing into a flower is an excellent image for this. Under the earth you cannot see the bulb sending out root tendrils or green shoots. The process is active and developing long before the shoot breaks the crust of dirt overhead. And once the stalk is through the dirt it still requires growth and development to flower.

   a. Draw a picture of your waiting and what stage it is in compared to a bulb that is planted in fall for the spring season.

   b. Each day consider whether there might have been a little progress, unseen to you.

   c. Affirm to yourself that growth is happening even though it is not visible to you at this time. Rooting around the bulb to make sure the roots are developing will only kill the bulb.

   d. When processes require time, our hardest task is to let them develop. Figure out what actions act like water and sun to the bulb and what actions might act like disturbance to the bulb.

2. Become comfortable with not knowing. You may feel some urgency to know the answer to important questions, such as, "Does he love me?" or, "Will I be accepted into the program?" If you are experiencing that,

   a. Ask yourself whether you have done what you can do for today. If not, get to it!

   b. Say to yourself, out loud, "I want to know and I don't know." Simply notice how you feel when you say that. Often acknowledging your want and the reality that you cannot have it now relaxes the tension. This is easy to do whether you are at work or at home because the focus is inside of you.

3. Long waits of weeks or months wear you down and increase the pressure to get moving or doing. This sense of pressure can distract you from doing what is in front of you for today and usually does not move you in the direction of your long term goal. Create some private time for calming down.

   a. You can use moments to breathe and clear your mind—even in the middle of a task or with a group of people you can simply redirect your attention from your wait to the tasks at hand.

b. Think calming and focusing thoughts that remind you the outcome is not in your control. Use the Serenity Prayer to determine if you should wait or take action and to remind you to ask for patience when you are agitated. The Serenity Prayer is:

> "[God] Grant me the Serenity
> to accept the things I cannot change,
> the Courage to change the things I can,
> and the Wisdom to know the difference."

If this reminds you to take an action you neglected, then do so, but this prayer will probably, in the case of waiting, remind you that you have taken all the action you can and that you must let it go for now.

4. Use other people to help you. Others often know you are waiting and are willing to help you distract yourself or offer comfort and support. Tell others exactly what they can do to support you, specifically telling then how often to call you, whether you want them to inquire or just let you bring it up, when you need to be distracted, whether you want alone time or someone to take you to a movie or bring you a meal.

5. Smile. Practice smiling a Mona Lisa type of smile for no apparent reason. Thich Nhat Hanh, the master of mindfulness, wrote that this increases inner wellbeing. It will make you look calm and eventually help you feel calm when you do it enough. An interesting little study examined the impact on people who used Botox to stop frown lines and the resulting inability to frown improved moods!

Waiting Attitudes

What are you waiting for at this time?

_____

_____

_____

_____

Is there anything you must do to move the waiting process along?

_____

_____

_____

_____

Identify the waiting attitude you believe you could practice in your current waiting situation:

_____

_____

_____

_____

Remember: No one needs to know you are waiting and no one will ever see the techniques you are applying unless you choose to tell them or use their encouragement.

Change Your Perspective

STEP #6

Change Your Perspective

In many respects, what you see is what you get, when it comes to your stress levels. And I mean this literally. One form of stress is caused by monotony. Looking at things the same way day after day is stress-inducing. It is dull or stifling or, worse, it is numbing. "Looking at things the same way" may be a metaphor for your attitude or a *literal* description of your work and living space. You may have the stress caused by dullness.

In some ways, life is easier when we don't have to think about things in a fresh way. Our brains know this and immediately assist us to form habits. Habit dictates how you arrange your workspace, tells you where to sit at the dinner table, where to ride in the family car, and even sends you to your preferred spot in a movie theater. Once upon a time, you chose or were assigned those places. And you kept them. There may be nothing wrong with these habitual spots. Habit certainly eliminates some squabbling between kids in a car and eliminates a conversation every time you go to a movie about where to sit.

The downside of this efficient habit is that sitting in the same seat keeps you looking at the same things. If you are in a job where you are on the move within a building or outside of a building, then you probably won't need this stress solution. You won't be stressed out by visual monotony. But for those of you who have a desk or cubicle and have not yet moved to a corner office with a view, consider the following points:

- Visual monotony is stressful.

- People are hardwired to be scanning their horizons for clues about how to navigate through the world.

- As the world became more industrial and technological, and people's work moved indoors, it apparently did not occur to the captains of industry that monotony is tedious, and tedium is detrimental to good work performance.

- Today, even though we know what monotony does, most businesses will not commit money to changing these circumstances.

Change your point of view. Looking at something from a different angle can change the whole situation. When you shift the view, you will

- Be more creative.

- Better able to solve a problem.

- Improve your mood.

- Improve your attitude.

Research demonstrates this. Getting a new view is a *literal*, not metaphorical, solution to your stress. Being outside and simply seeing the green of nature can stimulate the growth of new ideas. Research on a brain molecule, nitric oxide (NO), shows that when it is stimulated your neurons connect more readily, opening the possibility of new thoughts and creative problem solving. Simulating the release of NO can be done on purpose. Moving in rhythm, playing an instrument, getting into nature, getting a massage, doing a creative activity, even dancing and laughing can get NO going and get you that new perspective.

Fortunately, there are things you can do, no matter where you work, to provide visual stimulation that soothes the nerves and stimulates the eyes:

1. **Put live plants where you work.** Unless you have a "black thumb," being around live greenery is very soothing. Plants change on a daily basis so it provides a source of visual interest, especially if you choose blooming plants. Plants require a small amount of attention to note when they need watering or pruning or plucking of dead leaves. When you attend

to these small daily changes you will experience a subtle shift in your interest level whenever you look at the plant. This is a stress-busting break in monotony.

2. **Hang pictures or place objects of art in your workspace.** When you look at a piece of art, the color, the subject, the style will cause your thoughts to move. When your eyes come to rest on the art, it won't distract your attention from a conversation or from your work, but your mind will get a little jolt of interest, even if you only look long enough to blink and return to your work. If there is something about your art that grabs you, then your unconscious will get a tweak when you gaze at it. This is a change from the focus of your work, and breaks the stress of concentration or boredom. Don't let someone else decide how to decorate your space.

3. **Place pictures of family, friends, pets and favorite places around your workspace,** even if it means sticking them on the inside of a locker or tucking them next to your phone. Screensavers or wallpaper on phones, computers and tablets can give us glimpses of what we love to see: faces of loved ones, locations that bring us excitement or peace, and so on. Every time you see these, your mind will immediately relate to the person or place. Choose photos that remind you of a fun time or a person you love or a place that makes you smile when you recall it. You will find yourself momentarily having the good feeling about the person or place in the picture.

4. **Bring a remembrance into work.** Remembrances are the things people collect from places they visit: seashells, stones, beads or any small items. Remembrances call to mind the ambiance, the fun, the pleasure, the relaxation, the people, and the sights, sounds and smells. Remembrances elicit the whole experience when you glance at them, these pieces of the place you enjoyed. You can bring a remembrance to almost any work setting. Bring a memento of a special time and place it where you notice it periodically. There are electronic and social media ways to do this, such as the Facebook timeline that allows you to revisit previous good experiences. These can be a great mental and emotional diversion.

5. **Change where you sit or where you stand whenever you can.** If you have a sedentary job, regularly change your seat. Find ways to move the angle of a desk so you can sit at it differently. Use a different chair.

6. **Look out a window as often as possible.** The changes in the sky, the traffic, and the people on the street are all of interest and stimulate your visual senses. If you are lucky enough to be able to get outside once or several times a day, be sure to take advantage of time to look at the sky, and any evidence of nature you can see: trees and bushes, birds or animals, flowers or water. It will reduce stress brought on monotony.

Fix Monotony

What are 3 things you can do to change the impact of visual monotony in your work?

_____

_____

_____

Electronic:

_____

_____

_____

Outside environments to walk into or live plants:

_____

_____

_____

Art or mementos:

_____

_____

_____

When will you introduce them to your space?

_____

_____

_____

STEP #7

Eat!

STEP #7

Eat!

AHA! Were you hoping to see a recommendation to eat chocolate as a stress reliever? Actually, chocolate works quite well to make you feel better. Chocolate can raise dopamine levels in your brain better than any other food. Those are the brain chemicals that play a major role in feeling good. Regrettably, chocolate does have side effects—if only it had no weight gain or sugar high from eating it, everyone could use chocolate-eating as a stress solution.

Eating is comforting. When you eat, you are doing something good for yourself. Eating can be diverting and enjoyable. Taking time to eat can be an oasis in the desert of stress at work or at home..

Think about how you currently use eating at work or at home:

- Does eating give you a chance to sit down?

- Is eating the one activity that feels like it is just for you?

- Do you use eating at your desk to make the time pass?

- Do you eat to take a break away from the work station?

- Do you use eating as a chance to take a walk to the snack machine?

- Is eating your excuse to go to the break room and get away from the job?

Stress Eating. The high cost of eating to relieve stress is the new stress from excess weight. You feel sluggish or unattractive. You develop problems with health and well-being. Weight gain from stress-relief eating lowers your self-esteem. The temporary relief of the stress-eating results in higher long term stress.

Positive Stress Relief. Nourishment can replace depletion. Healthful eating can relieve stress. If you do it right, you won't have those negative side effects of weight gain and lowered self-esteem. **The secret is to use your eating to nourish yourself but attend to the process of eating by slowing down and appreciating the food.**

Nourish yourself with positive eating

Sweet relief increases stress. Nourishing yourself first requires choosing foods that do something good for your body. Sweets do have that temporary boost of tasting good, but they fall into the category of "tastes good but not good for you." They have little or no nutritional value. Sweets actually worsen feelings of stress, because they cause jolts of jittery energy and then cause crashes into fatigue. Does this sound like how you feel when you have that doughnut and coffee break? Sweets seem easy. Even though you could feel better about eating sweets if you bake your own desserts from health food recipes with lots of whole grains and nuts to get some nutrition with the sweet, for most of us it seems so much easier to stop at a doughnut shop or head for the vending machine. Even coffee drinks without the pastries may come with significant amounts of sugar even when they are not accompanied by pastry.

Some people are much more susceptible to those crashes than others. Fatigue caused by that blood sugar low (also called "sugar blues") feels like being tired. You might think it is the job and a snack is a cure. So, when you think about eating as a stress solution, you are going to look for better foods. Foods that nourish you will be foods that keep your blood sugar even so you do not experience those highs and lows, but rather feel a steady level of energy throughout the day. If you do not know much about the nutritional value of food, try reading a simple book on the subject. The internet has endless resources about nutrition, but if you are not well informed, don't start researching supplements. Pick instead a basic, but excellent volume such as Leanne Brown's *Good and Cheap: Eat Well on $4 a Day* or take a look at Andrew Weil's *Eating Well for Optimum Health.*

There are simple guidelines to use:

1. **Choose nutritious food.** It keeps you functioning at your best, will work as a source of fuel for your body (which might be drained more mentally than physically) and is often a source of pleasure to offset a dreary workday.

2. **In order for eating to be pleasurable and serve as a diversion, you have to notice you are eating.** Most people who have trouble controlling their weight have problems in enjoying their food to the fullest. You may not believe this until you try the following stress relieving tips to get true enjoyment from what you eat:

    *   **Chew.** Take time to chew every bite thoroughly. Chew until you are completely ready to swallow and do not put any other bite of food or drink into your mouth until you have swallowed. This is harder to do than you think if you are used to eating at your desk or while in a meeting or standing at a counter. The press of stress tells us to rush all day, and we rush our eating as well. If you chew, you will digest better, besides enjoying the process of eating more. And even if you are eating a candy bar as your lunch, because you are rushing from one task to the next, you can still chew it. You will notice and taste more, which are the next two tips.

    *   **Taste (T.A.S.T.E.) the morsel of food.** This is more possible when chewing slowly. T.A.S.T.E. stands for:

        Take time to eat
        Attend to the eating process
        Savor the flavor
        Talk to yourself about the nourishment
        Enjoy the eating

    *   **Notice that you are eating.** When you gobble food, no matter how nutritious it is, you increase your stress level, not relieve it. Don't eat while doing other things. Most people do this, and you will certainly

do it some of the time whether at work, home, or on the road. If you want your eating to really provide stress relief, pay attention to it. Do not read, watch TV, eat at your desk or eat in the car. At most, have a conversation with a family member or co-worker. This can be a big challenge in our fast food culture, but it will make your eating as stress-free and relaxing as possible.

3. **By all means use your breaks and mealtimes as diversion from the workday pace.** Too often people do not take breaks or lunches because of the high demand to get work out. Or they believe they must show their commitment to the work by not taking breaks, even for lunch. Skipping meals, eating too fast or on the job, or eating only snacks becomes a huge problem for health and increases stress.

4. **Eat foods you like, and by all means, prepare them ahead so they are ready for you when you get hungry.** Try to choose among those the foods which are least likely to spike your blood sugar too fast. If you eat a salad, put a protein in it and use dressings sparingly. Eat sandwiches with whole grain breads, never white bread, and try keeping apples, pears, carrot sticks or other fruits and vegetables which do not require refrigeration handy for the moments when you would otherwise reach for a bag of potato chips or a candy bar. Sometimes you just want something to chew on: it's comforting. So make sure you have options that are going to help you in the long run. If you have the right stuff prepared ahead, it is easier to choose it. Most snack machines have no fresh items of any kind.

5. **Avoid caffeine, sugar and aspartame (Nutrasweet is a brand name for aspartame), which intensify the jitteriness brought on by stress.** All of these chemicals are hard on your body as well as major contributors to jolting your blood sugar. So monitor the amount of soda and coffee you drink. Caffeine alone raises your blood sugar even with no cream or sugar added. Substitute herbal teas, hot or iced, for coffee and cola. Drink water with lemon. It is definitely more fun to get a cold soda from the machine, but the point here is stress reduction. Caffeine and sugar do not help lessen the stress load, no matter how much you wish they would.

6. **Be sure you are getting your vitamins.** You cannot build a healthy brain without them. If you are doing nothing, even a simple multi-vitamin will help. Many Americans are short on Vitamins D and B-12. A quick check with your physician can determine if you are one of them. And with those vitamins, make sure you get some high quality protein in your diet, preferably three times a day so you will have a constant stream of the components you need to build a healthy brain. Going beyond these guidelines for supplements is beyond the scope of this book, but you can check out Daniel Amen's *Change Your Brain, Change Your Life* or Brown, Gerbarg and Muskin's *How to Use Herbs, Nutrients and Yoga in Mental Health Treatment.* There is a lot of good material available in books and online. Just watch out for the inevitable advertising of people who push special diets, supplements and nutritional foods without good evidence that they help or that you may not really need. The diet and body-building industries are big business in the U.S.A.

Eating Habits

Notice: What are your current habits of eating, either at home or at work, when you feel under pressure?

_____

_____

_____

List the types of beverages, foods, and snacks you go after and the places/times you eat:

_____

_____

_____

Notice: When do you feel most satisfied with a meal?

_____

_____

_____

List two things you believe you could do starting tomorrow that would make your eating part of your stress solution:

_____

_____

_____

NOTES:

_____

_____

_____

Get Active

STEP #8
Get Active

Exercise as Both Relief and Prevention

Exercise. If you are about to skip reading this because you have heard it all before, you are exhibiting information burnout: a sign of *stress*! Rest assured you are not about to read about the joys of weight lifting or marathon running. This is about the kind of exercise that fits a stressed out life. A Stress Solution is meant to provide you with tools to decrease stress—not increase your stress.

You may already know about the benefits of daily vigorous exercise. I am going to describe some of those before telling you about other types of physical activity that will reduce stress. Your overall fitness helps you respond to the impact of unexpected stress. Physical fitness gives you the stamina to be resilient during extended periods of stress. Your heart rate will respond quickly and slow quickly. You will use your energy more efficiently.

Another benefit of vigorous exercise for stress management is that brain chemicals you need to feel good are stimulated by exercise. Those neurochemicals build over time to keep you feeling positive on a daily basis. Aerobic exercise generates positive feelings immediately from physical enzymes that are released but also because you know you did something that is for your benefit.

Physical fitness gives you stamina to handle stress

What you might not know is that a less aerobic kind of exercise—movement—is great as a short-term stress reduction method. This is why moving is important in your arsenal of stress solutions. Movement releases the built-up physical energy which results from tension, fear, anger, frustration, which are the emotions commonly accompanying stress. Have you ever sat in a meeting and bounced your leg or tapped a finger or at least observed it in someone who could not sit still? When you are feeling stressed out you want to move. If you are in a job that lets you move around a lot, physical releases may not be as important as they are for those who spend too much of the day sitting or standing in one place.

Increase your opportunities to move and get the most out of your movement. Shake off your stress energy rather than hold it inside! Try these ideas:

1. **Use any of many apps that remind you to stand, move and stretch.**

2. **Walk stairs.** You can walk stairs in most buildings whenever you have to go from one location to another. If you have to walk too many flights for a meeting, use the elevator for some but walk up a few floors before you catch the elevator. Likewise, if your destination is only a floor or two away, walk a few extra flights of stairs on your way to and from your destination. Whenever you take a break, you can also duck into a stairwell and go up and down a few floors. This will benefit you more than you can imagine. You will get the best out of this method if you walk the stairs briskly enough to get a little cardiovascular increase. Your energy will increase and you will feel more alert.

3. **Walk outside whenever possible.** Even if you can only go outside for a few minutes, it will clear the cobwebs and refresh you. Too often buildings have no windows to open for fresh air, employees don't have access to windows, or we work in spaces where we have more contact with mechanical or chemical smells than out of doors. With walking outside, the fresh air alone is good, but the contact with the earth while you move is also important. Even if you work where you can open windows, you will still need to get your body outside. Think about how you describe a very stable, calm person, "He really has his feet on the ground." This expression

captures the essence of someone who is grounded, whose response to stress is not evident in frenzied verbal or physical activity. You can get this kind of calm by literally putting your feet on the outside ground and feeling the earth. Get outside, even to take a quick trip to your car, e.g., to get your lunch out of the trunk, and as you walk, imaging your feet pounding your excess energy into the ground. Mother Earth can absorb any amount of energy you have to discharge. To prevent stress from building, regularly take every excuse to get outside for a few moments to clear your head and connect your feet to the earth.

4. **Pace in your work space. Stress can make you feel sluggish and sleepy even while it tends to make your body feel unpleasantly aroused.** Stress increases your heart rate, blood pressure and respiration, but doesn't result in that good energy you get when exercise is raising those rates. Diminish the effects of increased cardiovascular response to stress events by raising your level of cardiovascular energy through physical activity instead.

   - When you feel worked up, pace. Raise your arms overhead and swing them around a bit. Bend over, then stretch up. Sway back and forth. Swing your arms windmill style. Stand on one leg and shake the other loosely. Then shake the other leg. Shake out your arms the same way. This is not about fitness, but sending energy out of you and back into the environment from which it came.

   - You don't have to wait until you can get an hour at the gym with a trainer. Try the Tabata method for a 4-minute total body workout. There are various versions of this to watch online or get as an app.

   - Similarly, take a look at Toni Yancey's 10-minute "Instant Recess."

5. **Breathe like a smoker.** What? No, this is not a suggestion to go outside a back door and wheeze. Think about it. Smokers light up to let go of stress, and it is not entirely for the nicotine. If you are a smoker, try breathing through a straw as if through a cigarette, and see how this resembles the benefit you experience from getting a cigarette. If you are not a smoker, breathe deeply and then *focus on exhaling slowly and in a stream*. Breathing out lets tension go. When we breathe, the inhale opens up a feeling of being constricted. The exhale releases the tension. Whether

your respiration is increased by stress or not, just to notice the impact of exhaling, breathe but exhale as long as you can. While exhaling, imagine you are sending a stream of negative energy down and out through your feet. You will be surprised at the tension lowering.

6. **Do your regular exercise pattern during the day.** It is surprising how many people can arrange their work to take a midday break if they figure it out. Any time you can, take a longer break in the middle of the day. If you cannot get to a health club, take a long walk. If you work out at a health club go in the middle of the day if at all possible. Stay at work a little longer in the afternoon in exchange for the midday break. It will make the afternoon at the job feel more relaxed.

My Physical Fitness

Think for a moment about where you are at in your physical fitness. What are you currently doing on a regular basis?

- _____
  _____

- _____
  _____

- _____
  _____

- _____
  _____

- _____
  _____

- _____
  _____

- _____
  _____

- _____
  _____

If you already are getting the benefits of a good fitness program, you will just need to pay attention to the little stress relievers, but if you are not doing much now, read on.

Physical Activity to Prevent Stress:

Getting fit for stress management differs from achieving an aerobic or muscular ideal. Fitness programs are offered by endless books available at any bookstore. But for stress reduction purposes, do not be put off by the grocery checkout magazine array that proclaims the latest perfect workout each month. You do not have to stress out over what regimen to choose. All you have to do is walk. No special spandex outfits are required. No health club membership or fabulously expensive custom shoes are needed. Just take off the shoes that pinch, put on your comfy shoes and head around the block after dinner.

Walk!

As a stress solution, walking is enough. If your goal is to stimulate heart and lungs into healthful levels of activity, a brisk walk will give you 70% of the benefit of any other routine. When you are ready for the other 30% of total fitness you will have the energy to seek it out. (If you are in reasonably normal health, walking should pose no risk, but if you have any doubts, you ought to be consulting a doctor anyway. So go get a physical if you do not know for certain that you are healthy enough to walk.) Once you have established that, you do not have to start out with a full hour of arm-pumping power walking. That would discourage anyone who is moving from slippers to gym shoes after dinner.

Try the following ideas to improve your level of exercise. It will release enough tension to keep your stress levels down and your endorphins up. The goal of this kind of exercise is to feel less of the depressed and anxious feelings that result from stress and to improve your stamina.

1. Walk once around the block. If you have no motivation, but only suspect that there is some value in this walking idea, then don't expect more of yourself than to walk around the block once. Pick a time like just before breakfast, on your way to work, or right after dinner. Then get out there for just a few minutes.

2. Don't do more than you want. At the beginning, beyond making yourself do something, pay attention to what feels good to you. Do as little or as much as you want. If you force yourself to go once around the block but then feel like going twice around, go ahead. Just don't tell yourself that you *have to* do more. No need to whip yourself. You will like this so much after a while, that if you listen to your body, you will build at a pace that is healthy and increasingly aerobic.

   How will you know when you are doing enough?

   • You will feel enthusiasm.

   • You will miss walking if you do not get out.

   • You will feel perceptibly better physically and emotionally.

   • You will get the most fitness benefit and the most emotional well-being when you get your frequency up to five or six times per week, and increase the time of exercise to 25-45 minutes, with your heart beating in the lower aerobic range. The overall impact on your mood and your capacity to respond to stress will astound you.

3. Gradually increase a little more, both the distance and the pace at which you walk. The goal is indeed to increase, but to do so in ways that keep your motivation high.

Make Exercise Fun!

To keep enjoying it, notice what makes it fun. Find what you like so you will keep on walking! List some of those things here:

- ❑ Do you like the silence of being all alone?

- ❑ Do you like listening to music, audio books or podcasts while you go? (Keep it low enough to not hurt your ears, which are more sensitive while you are exercising than at other times.)

- ❑ Do you like having a walking partner to talk with?

- ❑ Do you like looking at landscaping ideas in the neighbors' yards?

- ❑ Do you like to listen for the birds?

- ❑ Do you like walking the neighborhood or do you want to go to a more natural setting?

- ❑ Do you like the fresh air, no matter what the temperature, or is there a mall that is open for walking in a safe and temperature-regulated environment?

What is your goal for changing your level of fitness?

_____

_____

_____

_____

_____

_____

_____

_____

Check in with yourself after four weeks. If you stopped, what has stopped you?

_____

_____

_____

_____

_____

_____

_____

_____

_____

If you have started, what are you noticing about the way you feel, and what do you want to keep up?

_____

_____

_____

_____

_____

_____

_____

_____

_____

_____

_____

_____

_____

Achieve Inner Peace

STEP #9

Achieve
Inner Peace

Inner Stress Reduction

Finding your spiritual center is not about religion. It is about your sense of connection to the greater realm around you. You may conceptualize this through your religious beliefs or you may sense this as connection to the energy of life, but we are all a part of something greater than ourselves. When you are grounded in that sense, you can use that to ease stress. Regardless of your spiritual orientation, even if you say you have no spiritual orientation, you have an inner life and a connection to the energy of life. This spiritual stress solution does not advocate a particular spiritual orientation. You may adapt the ideas to fit your particular expression of spiritual life.

> ## Your spiritual self is a connection to something greater than yourself

Life causes stress. Your stress level may boil over when the phone rings that one more time, or you forgot to buy milk for breakfast, or your ride to work is sick, or your kids call home to say they are running late. Sometimes the worst stress occurs as you start your day:

- Commuting to work

- Rushing to a sales call or the next repair call or the next meeting

- Making one more car pool trip than you can stand this week

Your spiritual self doesn't stay home when you go into a stressful environment. You can use everything you know about inner peace to be peaceful even in the moment that events conspire to make your life difficult. There is no need to have a quiet setting or special accompaniments like music or candles to use your spiritual tools for stress management.

Mindfulness

In recent years, the burgeoning research on the power of mindfulness has made it clear that practicing mindful awareness is a major aid to remaining peaceful. Without writing a treatise on it here, there are basic concepts that you can immediately apply, and then if you want to go on to practice mindful meditation you will be able to achieve even greater inner peace.

A primary principle of mindfulness is to be in this moment. That does not imply you never have a plan or that you never remember your history. It means that you live in the now. This is the moment you have. Notice it. Take it in. Mindfulness is a way of being present in day to day events in a focused and peaceful way that is foreign to stressed out people, but achievable by everyone. For example, consider eating an orange. How often do you focus on the juices bursting from the peel and the scent intensifying as you open the orange to eat? It is likely you are focused on the people you are talking to or the other activity you are trying to do at the same time, like reading or watching TV and, consequently, you are not present to the act of eating the orange.

When you are stressed out, you are anxious, and anxiety always leads to being in the past with your mistakes or in the future worrying about yet-to-occur problems instead of being in the present. Thich Nhat Hanh's books listed in the reading list will help you see how you can even use your daily work as a meditation. They will also help you decide how to incorporate some truly peaceful moments into your lifestyle.

Daniel Siegel writes in *The Mindful Brain: Reflection and Attunement in the Cultivation of Well-Being* that looking at experience with curiosity, openness, acceptance and love allows us to be in the moment, observing without judging. This stance is a centered, spiritual position that allows us to focus our attention and remain peaceful.

If you are stressing because the traffic is heavy on your way to work, it does not change the amount of traffic. Simply being in the moment, observing, and knowing that when you get to work, then you will be there eliminates the stress of putting yourself into a future moment when something else may be happening. Have you ever spent a bad commute feeling upset, heart pounding with the "OH, NO! I am going to be yelled at (be late for the meeting, get in trouble . . .)" thoughts racing through your mind, only to find out when you arrive that the boss is not there to notice or the meeting is canceled? You could have saved yourself all the distress by simply staying in the moment of commuting.

A second principle that is very important to inner peace is that you will withhold judgment. Do not make assumptions or judgments of good-bad or right-wrong while you are observing. Most stress comes from judging, i.e., "This should not be happening!" or, "You should not be doing that!" or, "This is awful!" And we make those judgments long before seeing how a situation plays out. We try to ascribe meaning to situations without fully understanding them, and that meaning affects our emotions and our stress levels. When we decide what something means, then our attitude about it is the outcome: and we stress ourselves with negative attitudes.

A psychiatrist named Viktor Frankl wrote profoundly on the subject of how our interpretations of experience are at the core of our well-being. In his book, *Man's Search for Meaning*, he develops this thinking. *"Everything can be taken from a man but one thing: the last of the human freedoms—to choose one's attitude in any given set of circumstances, to choose one's own way."* Our spiritual orientation determines a great deal of how we ascribe meaning to experience. Mindfulness allows us to take in the experience fully before assigning a meaning. A great deal of distress is avoided by holding back on judgment.

I recently was playing cards with other women, and I was becoming irritated with one of them (stressed out) until I stopped judging her and just observed her words and actions. No matter what occurred she found a way to make a negative remark. Even while walking across a long porch overlooking a lovely pond when one of the women remarked that the day was lovely, she responded, "Yes, but just wait. The humidity is rising and it will be awful later." Because I had shifted to observing, I no longer felt irritated. What I thought was, "Yes, perhaps, and it is lovely now. I wish for her that she could feel that." I did not need to take in her opinion. I did not need to decide if she was right or wrong or good or bad. I did not need to have a feeling about it at all. I just noticed that she said it. Then I paused to take longer breath of warm air and a longer look at the beautiful setting before returning inside.

Another important principle of mindfulness is to not be caught up in attachment to things or even to emotions. The desire, the wanting of things, can become an enormous stressor, and interruption of experiencing life as it is now. Whether you acquire or do not acquire what you long for, the state of longing is stressful. It is more peaceful to be in the now and take pleasure in what is here. Jon Kabat-Zinn is a current force for teaching and researching the power of mindfulness. In his book *Wherever You Go, There You Are: Mindfulness Meditation in Everyday Life* he wrote, "To let go means to give up coercing, resisting, or struggling, in exchange for something more powerful and wholesome which comes out of allowing things to be as they are without getting caught up in your attraction to or rejection of them, in the intrinsic stickiness of wanting, of liking and disliking."

Practicing mindful awareness is a pathway to spiritual peace while living in the here and now.

Compassion for Self and Others

Another component of inner peace is to allow our best self to be compassionate to ourselves and to others. Often it is easier to feel compassion for others. We can observe their suffering, imagine how we would feel if we were experiencing what they are going through and feel warm or caring toward them. Compassion often moves us to action to relieve the suffering of another person. Self-compassion is showing to ourselves the same consideration we would show others. That we stop harshly criticizing ourselves when we are not perfect. Such self-castigation, blame and dislike are major stressors!

A wonderful source of information about self-compassion, including a test to see how self-compassionate you are is at www.self-compassion.org, Kristin Neff's website. She offers several excellent guided meditations for self-compassion.

Connect to Inner Wisdom and Higher Power Through Prayer and Meditation

Use the following inner peace techniques for the management of immediate problems or for settling in the middle of a drawn-out hectic day.

Pray. Many readers will already use this if they are religious. If you believe in the power of prayer you may already be using it to get peace when things blow up in your face. This is why it is worth a try: The process of praying or turning to a Higher Power means asking for strength, help, calm, courage or wisdom. People who pray feel the strength of a Higher Power and it comforts, supports, encourages them. Many see prayers answered, and with that experience they engage the power of hope through prayer. Just asking can give you immediate access to your own inner wisdom as well as to the support of your higher power.

When you utter a prayer in response to stress, in addition to the power you draw on from outside of yourself, you also draw on the best of your inner self, because you are pausing to remember that you have wisdom and strength. So, pray for access to your strength as well as for access to the strength of your Higher Power.

Recite a calming prayer or mantra. The use of a repetitive, encouraging phrase is soothing to the soul and deeply connects you to the source of all peace through this meditative activity.

Stress often causes us to ruminate, to think over and over and over about the same worry without progressing in our thoughts. That rumination increases our stress. If you have to ruminate, pick a peaceful phrase to substitute! Wouldn't you rather be repeating, "Every day, in every way, I am getting better and better," than fretting, "Now what am I going to do about the mess I am in?"

Finding an inspirational message is an excellent calming tool. Or, you might find phrases that give you the message you need to hear often, such as, "I am strong and competent to handle any problems," or "I can face any complication with quiet and calm." Recite these to yourself when feeling pressure. You can certainly look for passages from your religion's holy book to inspire and create specific emotions such as comfort, joy, hope, or courage. But you can also go the way of technology and use an app or receive via email an inspirational quote for the day.

While apps and sources abound, some current sources for those are:

- www.brainyquote.com

- Lift

- Quotes is another app that offers inspiration

- Inspirational and Motivational Quotes—Daily Quote of the Day

Inspirational Message

Is there a particular verse or message you want to use for inspiration? Write it out and repeat it a few times:

_____

_____

_____

Is there an app or inbox-delivery of inspiration that you have found? Keep track for a week of how it makes you feel when you read the quote and this will help you decide whether it is worth it to keep it up. An emoticon approach (draw a little face with the hallmarks of interest, joy, excitement, peace) could work here to help track the impact of the response to daily inspiration. If you are really into record keeping, put a number between 1 (low) to 10 (high) next to the emoticon to indicate the degree of the emotion. Like this:

Monday:

"When I let go of what I am, I become what I might be."

-Lao Tzu   **+8**

Daily Inspiration

Monday: _____

_____

Tuesday_____

_____

Wednesday _____

_____

Thursday _____

_____

Friday _____

_____

Saturday _____

_____

Sunday _____

_____

Meditate. Taking time to clear your mind with a meditation may do you a world of good to both calm yourself and give you better access to creative problem solving. There are many ways to think of and use meditation. You may become interested in developing a meditative practice that includes a long period of meditation during each day. This has many health and emotional benefits, and it will probably require you to get some instruction and guidance to learn and grow in this practice. Look for information at the websites for Mark Waldman or Andrew Newberg as well as www.bensonhenryinstitute.org the Massachusetts General Hospital Institute for Mind Body Medicine. There are literally hundreds of apps and YouTube videos to take you through meditation but some that are well known and get good marks for helping novices:

- Headspace

- Calm

- Deep—A virtual reality "game" that uses breath to calm and focus your mind

- Muse—A device that gives you feedback on your meditation to increase the depth and time

However, there are other aspects of meditation that enter into your everyday attitude toward your work and your response to it. Two books by Thich Nhat Hanh in the reading list are beautifully written and present a host of clearly expressed ideas to help you follow even if you have never been formally exposed to meditation. He discusses mindfulness and meditation in ways that you can fit into your individual religious framework.

Using Affirmations

You have probably heard about affirmations and may already use them in your life. Affirmations are statements you make to encourage you to manifest (develop and bring into being) growth in all your thoughts and actions. Recite encouraging affirmations to yourself several times in a row, more than once a day, as a way to install a positive attitude. Please note: affirmations that are unbelievable or impossible will not give you that positive shift. If you affirm that a specific person will love you, such an affirmation will not control that person. But if you affirm "I am lovable and attract people to my warmth." You may well become lovable and attractive in ways that will draw people to you.

Affirm Growth and Learning. Celebrate your stress solutions even before they emerge. Stress can intensify any of your negative feelings toward other people. Stress increases your tendency to blame others for how you feel, for the pressure you feel, or for any problems you face. It is easier to think your problems would go away if others would just do the right thing, but blaming rarely changes the stress and never makes you feel better. It does not make you more resilient in your stressful circumstances.

No matter how true it seems that someone else is creating problems for you, you cannot make another person behave differently. People change only when they choose to. You will feel less stress when you pay attention only to your part of solving your problems. Use affirmations to decrease your negativity, such as, "I let go of blame and celebrate my ability to solve my problems." It does not matter if you know how you are going to solve the mess you are in. Just know in this moment that you will figure it out. You will feel better. Affirming your best qualities and highest aspirations will keep you from knuckling under to stress.

Affirm Choice. A major stress source is the feeling of being trapped. One type of affirmation is a conscious recognition of having choices. You might feel trapped by too little education or experience to move out of your dead-end job. You might feel trapped by family obligations such as little children relying on you, or sick parents living nearby. You might feel trapped by financial obligations you have assumed.

You walk this path by choice

In truth, you always have options. You may not choose to exercise the options but when you remember you have chosen the place you are, helps tolerate where you are at until you choose something else. In practice, this means recognizing you are going to stay in a stressful situation while you create a better option. For example, if your job is too stressful, you might affirm, "I could quit today and sell my house to afford living on a smaller salary, but I do not want to do that. I will choose to stay in this job for now."

You might have to affirm continuing to do something you do not want to do. For example, perhaps you do not want to take care of your sick mother, and you also will not choose other options such as putting her in a home or sending her to another relative. Therefore, you are choosing to care for her. As a single parent, living out the demands of working for income and raising the children, you might feel you have no choice. What if you acknowledge that you have the option to give the kids up for adoption or quit work and end up on welfare? Does it sound silly, even shocking, to think this way? Think about it this way. Those *are* options, and you have rejected them. Remind yourself that the current hard path you walk, you walk by choice, and you will be less stressed because you will feel less trapped.

Gratitude is an affirmation of appreciation for what you have now. In all ways that you promote access to your spiritual strength you are improving your attitude. Attitude is all the difference between contentment and aggravation. Which would you rather feel? It is your choice more often than you believe.

Many spiritual programs focus on *The Attitude of Gratitude*, meaning that paying attention to what is right, good, satisfying and positive is much more useful to our well-being than focusing on the negative. Researchers like Robert Emmons and Sonya Lyubormisky have found that people who practice gratitude as a daily or regular spiritual practice are more content and they are more likely to have healthy habits and be positively engaged with other people. They sleep better, feel better and manage stress better. You can keep a gratitude journal by your bedside and, every evening, write down three things that you feel grateful for. You will fall asleep aster and stay asleep better if you do.

The best practice of daily gratitude is now easier to remember by taking advantage of apps, most of which allow adding pictures and most of which are interactive if you want them to be. There are so many to choose from, but a few of those apps are:

- Gratitude Journal 365 Pro—very nice way to use pictures

- Gratitude Journal, which has a reminder feature and a daily quote

- Happier—Focuses on interacting with others about what is fun and happy in your life and keeps a record

Making Choices

What problematic situation in your life do you feel you have no choice about? List it here:

_____

_____

_____

_____

List every option, even if you would not choose those options. (This is a lot like brainstorming).

_____

_____

_____

_____

_____

_____

_____

Which option do you choose at this time? Write an affirmation of that choice:

_____

_____

_____

_____

Daily Affirmations

Consider the attitude that you want to maintain about contentment with your life. Write an affirmation that will remind you to nurture that attitude daily:

_____

_____

_____

_____

_____

_____

How will you nurture your *Attitude of Gratitude?*

_____

_____

_____

_____

_____

_____

_____

_____

_____

_____

_____

_____

_____

_____

STEP #10

Play!

STEP #10
Play!

Think about the laughing, joking or teasing types of people you know. How do they handle their stress? They laugh it off. They joke with their friends and co-workers. Light-hearted people take the position that anything can be a game, and in general, events and objects around them are pressed into use for fun even while working.

Children Need Recess, but So Do Adults

But really now, play? At work? Yes! Google figured that out when they got started; their workplaces, where people reportedly work very long hours, are also full of play of all kinds. Employees are encouraged to get creative using fun and movement, toys and gadgets. While I do not advocate living at work, the idea of encouragement to take a creativity break is one I love.

If you are not playful by nature, you can still get the benefits of playing around as a solution to your stress. Play is really just a diversion from the stressful moment that makes you feel lighter or causes you to forget the trouble. Play for adults is also called leisure time. You can play by regularly changing your perspective through hobbies or activities that take your mind away from your daily worries. Herbert Benson, in his book *The Breakout Principle*, discussed the importance of taking a break from work to play and enjoy music, movement and nature for stimulating the release of nitric oxide (NO). That is the brain's molecule to help you find new ideas and creative solutions to problems by helping neurons connect more freely with each other.

How do you find that diversion? Look for new forms of stimulation that do not have any destructive side effects, for your daily relaxation. I know several men who play basketball on their lunch hour. I think they are having more fun than they would lifting weights alone early in the morning. Some of these ideas are possible in small breaks and some might require more time:

- Do something with your hands. Anything you do with your hands might serve to divert: There are a great variety of little mind puzzles that you can work with your hands along the lines of a Rubik's Cube, or those metal twists. You can build furniture, make stained glass, needlepoint, or cross stitch or knot or create crafts or draw or build models.

- Mental changes of pace, such as writing poetry or journaling, working word puzzles or logic puzzles of all types can divert and entertain your mind.

- Do something physical. Shoot buckets, play badminton, join a volleyball or softball team. Prefer low impact? Find a video to dance along to. Moving in rhythm is great for stimulating mental activity.

- Play a musical instrument of any kind.

- Get involved in something totally opposite from your daily tasks. If you have to think all day, try cooking, gardening or even just having indoor plants to putter with.

Encourage Your Own Playfulness

Having a playful heart and taking playtime are two ways to lighten any load. Moments of play are not reserved for kids. Why does play relieve stress? You play because you want to. "Have to" disappears when you play. Playing is a total change from what you were doing. For example, if you sit at a computer all day, you might find diversion in sitting back from your desk and juggling small cloth balls for a few moments or manipulating heavy balls, like the Chinese medicine balls, in your hands. (Those have value for acupressure as well as stress release.) In other countries, men have used worry beads for years and years as a way to discharge energy through the movement of their fingers. Toy stores abound with items like these for entertainment.

Interact with others. Play often involves interacting with others and laughing. Happy interactions make us feel good. This is a real shift from focusing on a tough or unpleasant work situation. Do you have the chance to stop and talk, laugh or tell jokes with your co-workers?

People sing, hum or whistle while they work. Why? It is a solution to getting stressed out when the work is humdrum. You might feel shy about that, but playing music is an alternative to singing yourself. Sing along in your mind if you feel shy about singing out loud.

Barbara Frederickson began researching the importance of positive emotions many years ago, and she writes in her book *Love 2.0: finding Happiness and Health in Moments of Connection* about the power of our positive interactions with others for soothing our sprits and lowering our stress, but also the power of those interactions to lift us up. She has shown that even "micro-moments" of connection have the power to influence our health. She is the major contributor to the body of knowledge that states that positive emotions increase our resilience. They make us less likely to suffer stress. She notes that we can deliberately gain access to emotions like curiosity, awe, joy and love and the more we do that, the more content, resilient, wise and healthy we will be. That sounds awfully good, and is surprisingly not hard to do.

Now, if you are someplace where you can close your eyes, read these instructions and then imagine: Let yourself remember what it was like for each of the five senses: what would you see, smell, taste, hear, and touch or feel? Enjoy that for a few moments, then return to your work. You will feel refreshed. Of course, you can regulate the amount of time you spend on this, but even a short daydream can break monotony or reduce overwhelmed feelings.

Take a five senses vacation

Find nature to look at. For years, people have suggested visualizing or vividly imagining peaceful locations or experiences as a way of taking yourself away. Try it! It works! And at times it is even better if you can be in or at least look at nature. If you have access to a window either in your work area or nearby, try looking at the sky (not the sun) with your eyes, or close your eyes if there aren't windows. If you can see greenery or water, gaze on that.

Develop Positivity

Playfulness is inspired by and results in joy. You can nurture those experiences deliberately. Time with family and friends, playing with pets, especially engaging in play with children are sources of joyful inspiration.

If you are not quite ready to feel this good, try the loving kindness meditation on Barbara Frederickson's website, www.positivityresonance.com. You will feel much greater positivity toward yourself and others!

Visualize for a Mental Break

One of the simplest ways to gain access to positive emotions is to remember those you have had. Let your mind wander to a location or an event you really enjoy. Identify an event you really would like to remember:

_____

_____

_____

_____

_____

_____

_____

_____

_____

_____

_____

_____

_____

_____

_____

_____

_____

_____

_____

_____

_____

_____

Developing Positivity

Playfulness is inspired by and results in joy. You can nurture those experiences deliberately. What are your best temporary diversions or playing around options at work or at home when you are busy with housekeeping? List a few here:

_____

_____

_____

_____

Playing is not the only positive. If nothing comes to mind, remember awe, gratitude, hope, amusement, for other choices. Find a positive emotion to contemplate. Think back to when you really had a good time. Where were you, who was with you, what were you doing? Remember the emotions you had. Scan the experience with your five senses.

_____

_____

_____

_____

_____

_____

_____

Now what can you do in the future that will recreate any aspect of that: the people, the emotions, the sensory experience? Any one part of it is good, and several aspects of the experience are even better.

_____

_____

_____

_____

_____

_____

NOW: COMMIT! What can you do to encourage positivity:

Today

_____

_____

_____

_____

This Week

_____

_____

_____

_____

Do my electronic activities count? In this culture, we are increasingly focused on electronic sources of entertainment, yet few people are aware of how stressful these can be. On a daily basis, we might come home from a day of work and need some play time. The best advice is, first of all, do not use online shopping, gambling or other sources to spend money. Also video games, which can be fun, have only a very limited place in the realm of healthy stress solutions.

One young client told me about coming home from work and, feeling stressed, he decided he would watch TV while finishing up emails from work. What he realized was even though he thought he would not feel stress of working, he actually increased his stress: the work he was doing took a long time because he was distracted by TV, so he felt as if he were working all night (and he was). But he also felt stress because he did not catch all of the story he thought would be diverting. He agreed that if he absolutely had to work from home, he would go into a quiet place and work without distraction on work, then join his wife for TV where he could relax with her and take in the story. Within days he realized he felt less stress and more pleasure.

- Computer games and video games don't qualify as stress solutions, because for most people they actually increase stress. Those games elevate your blood pressure and function as a stimulant to your system. If you feel under-stimulated, go ahead and play; but if you are over-stimulated, video games are not a good choice.

- Shopping is not a stress reducer. You may be like many Americans who shop and spend as a way to feel better. Shopping done this way is like using drugs to feel better. The long-term consequence (debt, over-consumerism, value through possessions) is not worth the short-term boost.

Get interested in something new: stamps, trains, gardens, fishing, cooking, sports participation, or any other form of a hobby that takes you away from the world of stress-inducing activity; make sure you give yourself plenty of time to have fun. Those long-term, total diversion activities also can be a fabulous stress reliever. Nurture your interest in activities you enjoy, even if you can only do them at a restricted level at this particular time. For example, you can develop your interest in flowers by having a four-season garden in your yard, but what if you cannot manage a garden right now? You could begin to nurture that interest by having a few pots of plants in your office, and diverting yourself by gazing at the blooms during the day. Or, arrange flowers once a week and look at them the rest of the week. Maybe you like to gather wild plants, dry them and turn them into craft projects, or make your own paper or grow your own food. There are endless variations on this theme of developing your interests, from tying fishing flies to origami to learning to build furniture.

Have a pet. Your relationship with your pet may engender some of the most playful moments you will ever have. The benefits of having pets around have been researched and the results are amazing. A large company investigated differences in workers when they had a dog in the office. Where people were working at computers in cubicles, having a pet that stopped by to be petted or nuzzled them as they worked relieved tension. The stress-busting benefits of owning pets is also well documented.

Then Get Started! Whenever you are ready you can begin, and here's to a life with less stress and more fun!

Give Yourself Plenty of Time to Have Fun

You will have more success letting fun combat stress if you have reminders handy at first, until you get used to this. List four things you could do for *a few minutes at a time* that are fun for you:

1. _____

2. _____

3. _____

4. _____

Give some thought to your activities away from the office that are diverting, not required by life at home. TV and Internet do not count! It's okay to name things that require a partner, like cards or dancing, but be sure these are things you could pursue if you decide you want to!

What will you begin to do today to have more fun in your life?

_____

_____

_____

_____

_____

_____

_____

_____

_____

Create Your Reading List

Bibliography

For your convenience, you may download a PDF version of the handouts in this book from our dedicated website: www.pesi.com/ShiftStress

Amen, D., M.D., Routh, L. (2015). *Change your brain, change your life.* Harmony Books: New York.

Baker, Dan. (2004). *What happy people know.* St Martins-Griffin: New York.

Benson, H. and Proctor, W. (2003) *The breakout principle.* Scribner & Sons: New York.

Brown, L. (2015) Good and Cheap: Eating Well on $4 a day. Workman Publishing Company: New York.

Brown, R. Gerberg, P. & Muskin, P. (2012). *How to use herbs, nutrients and yoga in mental health care.* W.W. Norton: New York

Childre, D., Martin, H. (1999). TheHeartmath solution. Harper Collins: San Francisco. 1999.

Childre, D., Rozman, D. (2008) *Transforming anxiety: The Heartmath solution for overcoming fear and worry and creating serenity.* New Harbinger Publications: Oakland, CA.

Cornell, A.W. (1996). *The power of focusing.* New Harbinger Publications: Oakland, CA.

Ensley, E. (2007). *Prayer that relieves stress and worry.* Contemplative Press.

Davis, M &, McKay, M. (2012) The Relaxation and Stress Reduction Workbook.

Fredrickson, B. (2009). *Positivity.* New York: Crown Publishing

Fredrickson, B. (2013) *Love 2.0: How our supreme emotion affects everything we feel, think and do.* Hudson Street Press: London, England.

Hanh, T.N. (1975). *The miracle of mindfulness.* Beacon Press:Boston, MA.

Hanh,T.N.. (2010). You are here: Discovering the magic of the present moment. Shambala Publications: Boulder, CO.:

Newberg, A.,Waldman, M.R. (2009) *How God changes your brain.* Neff, K. (2015) Self-compassion: *The power of being kind to yourself.* Harper-Collins: New York.

Siegel, D.(2007). *The mindful brain: Reflection and attunement in the cultivation of well-being.* W.W. Norton & Co.:New York.

Weil, Andrew, M.D. (2000) *Eating well for optimal health.* Knopf: New York.

Other Books by Margaret Wehrenberg

The Anxious Brain

The 10 Best-Ever Anxiety Management Techniques

The 10 Best-Ever Anxiety Management Techniques Workbook

The 10 Best-ever Depression Management Techniques

Anxiety + Depression; Effective Treatment of the Big Two Co-Occurring Disorders

The 10 Best Anxiety Busters

Tough-to-Treat Anxiety